CU00959085

COUNTRY HERITAGE SERIES

Flowers

of the British Countryside

W.J. Gordon

ILLUSTRATED BY

John Allen

OMEGA BOOKS

PLATE 1

INTRODUCTION.

T HE present work fulfils well the object embraced in the title. It is not the first attempt to place before our contemporaries an easy method of ascertaining the botanical name of any species of British wild flowers; but others have been mostly of a briefer character and supplied but little else than the name of the plant. One need hardly observe that whoever cares to know the botanical name of a wild flower should make a point of knowing a great deal more about it, in fact everything he can; and one feature of importance in this little work is the description of the "Natural Orders" or "Families" (pp. 35 and 82, *et seq.*). For every beginner should make a point of studying thoroughly some types, such as are figured in the plates, of as many families as possible; and at the same time make himself familiar with their order of sequence according to the Natural System of Classification, which Mr. GORDON has followed.

It is unfortunately the case, with which teachers are only too familiar, that beginners are apt to rest contented with the name of a plant only. Such can never become botanists; and although the present work does not profess to grant more than "a nodding acquaintance with the wild flowers we meet with" (p. 16); yet the author encourages the beginner to advance further. This he must do with the aid of a "Flora" such as Hooker's "*Student's Flora of the British Isles.*

One must not look for more than the author proposes to give. Consequently, when the student has become familiar with the structure or morphological details of flowers by which they may be distinguished, he must proceed to the task of unravelling the mystery of their forms; and that is the methods of fertilization, which afford the clue to the various structures; as all flowers are adapted either to Self-fertilization, Wind-fertilization, or Insect-fertilization. The literature on this branch of botanical knowledge is very extensive; and the reader will, no doubt, find access to such works as Darwin's *Fertilization of Orchids, Forms of Flowers*, &c., as well as H. Müller's *Fertilization of Flowers*, and the present writer's *Origin of Floral Structures by Insect and other Agencies*. The study of this branch of physiology will be found to add very materially to the interest of the student, as it is always desirable, if possible, to know the "why" and the "wherefore" of any facts with which we may be familiar.

To explain this a little more fully, we may take, for example, the family Ranunculaceæ, the first in classification and with which the beginner will probably be first acquainted. A Buttercup has a flower with the petals widely spreading; so that it has been observed to be visited by more than sixty species of insects. Hence the pistils of the flowers on any plant can be easily fertilized by the pollen derived from those of another plant. It is thus adapted to insects and can be "crossed." It may consequently be called an insect-fertilized flower.

As, however, the stigmas are mature simultaneously with the anthers of at least some of its stamens, it can easily be self-fertilized in the absence of insect visitors.

On the other hand the Aconite with its great hooded sepal has only two petals, and these are connected with honey-secreting "nectaries" concealed within the hood. Consequently it is by no means so easy of access, and only a few kinds of humble-bee can properly extract the honey and "pollinate" the flower at the same time. Moreover, as the stigma is late in maturing, it does not readily, even if it be at all able to, set seed on its own account, that is by self-fertilization.

As an example of complete self-fertilization we may take the Celery-leaved Ranunculus or *R. sceleratus*. This species has minute blossoms, easily overlooked by insects. It seeds abundantly and is widely dispersed.

When we compare the rarity or commonness of plants—for setting seed is the only use of flowers to plants—the rule is that self- and wind-fertilized plants are by far the most abundant and wide-spread, while those which have become so modified that the flowers actually exclude all but a few kinds of insects, are greatly restricted in their distribution.

The above is but a sample, as a hint to the beginner to see what a wide field of observation is before him if he will but persevere and follow it out ; for *cæteris paribus*, every family furnishes material for similar observations.

In conclusion I can but hope the present work will prove as useful as it ought to be, and help the beginner over the initial but often troublesome stage of finding out the name of a plant and where to locate it in the Vegetable Kingdom. Having done this *his real work begins,* and that is to study his plant in all its stages till he can find out nothing new about it.

George Henslow

CONTENTS.

First published as *Our Country's Flowers* by Simpkin, Marshall,
Hamilton, Kent & Co. Ltd.

This edition published 1988 by Omega Books Ltd,
14 Greville Street, Hatton Garden, London EC1.

ISBN 1-85007-014-8

Printed and bound in Spain by Gráficas Estella, Navarra.

CHAPTER I.

LOCAL NAMES.

I N this list are the ordinary English names of our country's flowers. Against them are set the names under which the flowers are described in this book, which were given them to allow of their identification by the educated people of all nations, and which are just as easy to remember, and in most cases no more difficult to pronounce than the others. The identification of plants by their local names alone is almost impossible, for in the first place the nomenclature is not systematic, and gives no hint as to grouping, and in the second place, as will be seen from this list, in many cases very different plants have the same name, and in other cases many different names are borne by the same plant.

Aaron's Beard,
Hypericum calycinum.

Aaron's Rod,
Verbascum thapsus.

Abele,
Populus alba.

Absinth,
Artemisia absinthium.

Ache Weed,
Ægopodium podagraria.

Aconite,
Aconitum napellus.

Adam and Eve,
Arum maculatum.

Adam's Flannel,
Verbascum thapsus.

Adder Spit,
Pteris aquilina.

Adderwort,
Polygonum bistorta.

Adder's Fern,
Polypodium vulgare.

Adder's Flower,
Lychnis diurna.

Adder's Grass,
Orchis mascula.

Adder's Meat,
Arum maculatum.

Adder's Tongue,
Ophioglossum vulgatum.

Agleaf,
Verbascum thapsus. '

Agrimony,
Agrimonia eupatoria,

Agworm,
Stellaria holostea.

Alder,
Alnus glutinosa.

Alder Buckthorn,
Rhamnus frangula.

Ale-hoof,
Nepeta glechoma.

Alexanders,
Smyrnium olusatrum.

Alkanet,
Anchusa officinalis.

Allbone,
Stellaria holostea.

Allgood,
Chenopodium bonus-henricus.

Allheal,
Prunella vulgaris.

Allseed,
Radiola millegrana.

Alsike,
Trifolium hybridum.

Alysson,
Alyssum maritimum.

Amaranth,
Amaranthus blitum.

Amber,
Hypericum perforatum.

American Cress,
Barbarea præcox.

Andurion,
Eupatorium cannabinum.

Angle-berry,
Lathyrus pratensis.

Apple,
Pyrus malus.

Apple Mint,
Mentha rotundifolia.

Apple Pie,
Epilobium hirsutum.

Arbute,
Arbutus unedo.

Archangel,
Lamium galeobdolon, L. album, or Stachys sylvatica.

Argemone,
Potentilla anserina.

Argentine,
Potentilla anserina or Onopordum acanthium.

Arn,
Sambucus nigra.

Arrowgrass,
Triglochin (the genus).

Arrowhead,
Sagittaria sagittifolia.

B

Arrowroot,
Arum maculatum.

Asarabacca,
Asarum europæum.

Ash,
Fraxinus excelsior.

Avens,
Geum (the genus).

Averil,
Narcissus pseudo-narcissus.

Awl wort,
Subularia aquatica.

Azalea,
Loiseleuria procumbens.

Baccobolts,
Typha latifolia.

Baconweed,
Chenopodium album.

Baldmoney,
Meum athamanticum.

Balewort,
Papaver somniferum.

Balm,
Melissa officinalis.

Balsam,
Impatiens noli-me-tangere.

Band Plant,
Vinca major.

Baneberry,
Actæa spicata.

Banewort,
Atropa belladonna.

Barber's Brush,
Dipsacus sylvestris.

Barberry,
Berberis vulgaris.

Barley,
Hordeum (the genus).

Barnabas,
Centaurea solstitialis.

Barrenwort,
Epimedium nigrum.

Base Broom,
Genista tinctoria.

Base Rocket,
Reseda luteola.

Basil,
Calamintha clinopodium.

Basil Thyme,
Calamintha acinos.

Beak Rush,
Rhyncospora (the genus).

Beaked Parsley,
Anthriscus vulgaris.

Beam,
Pyrus aria.

Bearberry,
Arctostaphylos uva-ursi.

Beard Grass,
Polypogon (the genus).

Bear's Foot,
Helleborus fœtidus.

Bedwen,
Betula alba.

Bedstraw,
Galium mollugo.

Beebread,
Trifolium pratense.

Bee Orchis,
Ophrys apifera.

Beech,
Fagus sylvatica.

Beech-fern,
Polypodium phegopteris.

Bee's-nest,
Daucus carota.

Beet,
Beta maritima.

Beggar's Basket,
Pulmonaria officinalis.

Beggar's Blanket,
Verbascum thapsus.

Beggar's Buttons,
Arctium lappa.

Beggar's Needle,
Scandix pecten-veneris.

Bell-bind,
Convolvulus sepium.

Bell-bottle,
Hyacinthus non-scriptus.

Belleisle,
Barbarea præcox.

Bell-flower,
Campanula (the genus).

Bell Heather,
Erica tetralix.

Bell Rose,
Narcissus pseudo-narcissus.

Bell ware,
Zostera marina.

Ben,
Silene inflata or Senecio
jacobæa.

Bennels,
Phragmites communis.

Bennet,
Geum urbanum.

Bent Grass,
Agrostis vulgaris or Aira
flexuosa.

Betony,
Stachys betonica.

Betony (St. Paul's),
Veronica serpyllifolia.

Bifoil,
Listera ovata.

Bigold,
Chrysanthemum segetum.

Bilberry,
Vaccinium myrtillus.

Bindweed,
Convolvulus sepium.

Birch,
Betula alba.

Bird Briar,
Rosa canina.

Bird Cherry,
Prunus padus.

Bird Eagles,
Cratægus oxyacantha.

Bird Grass,
Poa trivialis.

Bird's Eye,
Primula farinosa.

Bird's Eyes,
Veronica chamædrys.

Bird's Foot,
Lotus corniculatus.

Bird's Nest,
Daucus carota or Mono-
tropa hypopitys.

Birthwort,
Aristolochia clematitis.

Bishopswort,
Stachys betonica.

Bistort,
Polygonum bistorta.

Bitter Cress,
Cardamine (the genus).

Bittersweet,
Solanum dulcamara **or**
Spiræa ulmaria.

Bitter Vetch,
Orobus (the genus).

Blackberry,
Rubus fruticosus.

Black Bryony,
Tamus communis.

Black Cap,
Typha latifolia.

Black Grass,
Alopecurus agrestis.

Black Heart,
Vaccinium myrtillus.

Black Heath,
Erica cinerea.

Black Hellebore,
Astrantia major.

Black Horehound,
Ballota nigra.

Blackthorn,
Prunus spinosa.

Blackwort,
Symphytum officinale.

Bladder Campion,
Silene inflata.

Bladder Fern,
Cystopteris (the genus)

Bladderwort,
Utricularia (the genus).

Blaeberry,
Vaccinium myrtillus.
Blanket,
Verbascum thapsus.
Bleeding Heart,
Cheiranthus cheiri.
Bleeding Willow,
Orchis morio.
Blewart,
Veronica chamædrys.
Blind Nettle,
Lamium (the genus).
Blinks,
Montia fontana.
Blite,
Suæda maritima.
Bloodroot,
Potentilla tormentilla.
Blooming Sally,
Epilobium angustifolium.
Blowball,
Taraxacum officinale.
Blue-ball,
Scabiosa succisa.
Blue Bell,
Hyacinthus non-scriptus.
Blue Bonnet,
Centaurea cyanus.
Blue Eyes,
Veronica chamædrys.
Blue Kiss,
Scabiosa succisa.
Blue Money,
Anemone pulsatilla.
Blue Weed,
Echium vulgare.
Blush Wort,
Erythræa (the genus).
Boar Thistle,
Carduus lanceolatus or C. arvensis.
Bog Asphodel,
Narthecium ossifragum.
Bog Myrtle,
Myrica gale.
Bog Nut,
Menyanthes trifoliata.
Bog Rhubarb,
Petasites vulgaris.
Bog Rush,
Schœnus nigricans.
Bog Strawberry,
Comarum palustre.
Bog Violet,
Pinguicula vulgaris.
Bolts,
Trollius europæus.
Bone Set,
Symphytum officinale.
Boodle,
Chrysanthemum segetum.

Boor's Mustard,
Thlaspi arvense.
Borage,
Borago (the genus).
Bottle Brush,
Equisetum (the genus), or Hippuris (the genus).
Bouncing Bet,
Saponaria officinalis.
Box,
Buxus sempervirens.
Bracken,
Pteris aquilina.
Brake,
Pteris aquilina.
Bramble,
Rubus (the genus).
Brandy Bottle,
Nuphar lutea.
Brandy Mint,
Mentha piperita.
Brassock,
Sinapis arvensis.
Bread and Milk,
Cardamine pratensis.
Briar,
Rosa (the genus).
Bride's Laces,
Phalaris arundinacea.
Bride wort,
Spiræa ulmaria.
Bright Meadow,
Caltha palustris.
Bristle Fern,
Trichomanes radicans.
Brome Grass,
Bromus (the genus).
Brooklime,
Veronica beccabunga.
Brookweed,
Samolus valerandi.
Broom,
Sarothamnus (the genus).
Broomrape,
Orobanche (the genus).
Brotherwort,
Thymus serpyllum.
Bryony,
Bryonia dioica or Tamus communis.
Buckbean,
Menyanthes trifoliata.
Buckler Fern,
Lastræa (the genus).
Buckrams,
Allium ursinum.
Buck's horn,
Coronopus (the genus).
Buckthorn,
Rhamnus catharticus, or Prunus spinosa.

Buckwheat,
Polygonum dumetorum.
Bugle,
Ajuga reptans.
Bugloss,
Echium vulgare, or Lycopsis arvensis
Bullace,
Prunus insititia.
Bull Daisy,
Chrysanthemum leucanthemum.
Bullock's Eye,
Sempervivum tectorum.
Bulrush,
Typha latifolia or Scirpus (the genus).
Burdock,
Arctium lappa.
Bur Marigold,
Bidens (the genus).
Burnet,
Sanguisorba officinalis.
Burnet Rose,
Rosa spinosissima.
Burnet Saxifrage,
Pimpinella saxifraga.
Bur Reed,
Sparganium ramosum.
Bur Weed,
Galium aparine.
Butcher's Broom,
Ruscus aculeatus.
Butter and Eggs,
Linaria vulgaris.
Butter Bur,
Petasites vulgaris.
Buttercup,
Ranunculus (the genus).
Butterfly Orchis,
Habenaria bifolia.
Butter Root,
Pinguicula vulgaris.
Butter-wort,
Pinguicula (the genus).
Button Hole,
Scolopendrium vulgare.
Buttons,
Tanacetum vulgare.

Cabbage,
Brassica oleracea.
Cadweed,
Heracleum sphondylium.
Calamint,
Calamintha (the genus).
Cammock,
Ononis arvensis.
Camomile,
Anthemis (the genus), or Matricaria (the genus).
Campion,
Lychnis (the genus), or Silene (the genus).

Canary Grass,
Phalaris canariensis.

Candlemas Bells,
Galanthus nivalis.

Candle Rush,
Juncus communis.

Candle Wick,
Verbascum thapsus.

Candy Tuft,
Iberis (the genus).

Cane Apple,
Arbutus unedo.

Canker,
Rosa canina, Papaver rhœas, or Senecio jacobæa.

Canterbury Bell,
Campanula trachelium.

Caper Spurge,
Euphorbia lathyris.

Capillaire,
Adiantum capillus-veneris.

Caraway,
Carum carui.

Care,
Pyrus aucuparia.

Carl Hemp,
Cannabis sativa.

Carlin Heather,
Erica cinerea.

Carline Thistle,
Carlina vulgaris.

Carrot,
Daucus carota.

Catchfly,
Silene (the genus).

Catchweed,
Asperugo procumbens.

Catwood,
Euonymus europæus.

Catwhin,
Genista anglica.

Cat's Ear,
Hypochœris (the genus).

Cat's Foot,
Nepeta glechoma.

Cat's Tail Grass,
Phleum pratense.

Celandine,
Chelidonium majus, or Ranunculus ficaria.

Celery,
Apium graveolens.

Centaury,
Erythræa centaurium or Centaurea cyanus.

Chaffweed,
Centunculus minimus.

Charlock,
Sinapis arvensis.

Chequer Lily,
Fritillaria meleagris.

Chequer Tree,
Pyrus torminalis.

Cherry,
Prunus cerasus.

Chervil,
Chærophyllum bulbosum, or Tordylium maximum.

Chicory,
Cichorium intybus.

Chickweed,
Stellaria media.

Chives,
Allium schœnoprasum.

Churchbroom,
Dipsacus sylvestris.

Cicely,
Myrrhis odorata.

Cinquefoil,
Potentilla reptans.

Clary,
Salvia pratensis.

Cleavers,
Galium aparine.

Cliff Rose,
Armeria maritima.

Clithe,
Arctium lappa.

Cloudberry,
Rubus chamæmorus.

Clove Pink,
Dianthus caryophyllus.

Clover,
Trifolium (the genus).

Clown's Mustard,
Iberis amara.

Club Moss,
Lycopodium (the genus)

Club Rush,
Scirpus (the genus).

Cock's Comb,
Rhinanthus crista-galli.

Cock's Foot,
Dactylis glomerata.

Codlings and Cream,
Epilobium hirsutum.

Colewort,
Brassica oleracea.

Coltsfoot,
Tussilago farfara.

Columbine,
Aquilegia vulgaris.

Comfrey,
Symphytum officinale.

Cool-tankard,
Borago officinalis.

Coral Root,
Corallorhiza (the genus).

Coral Wort,
Dentaria bulbifera.

Cord Grass,
Spartina stricta.

Coriander,
Coriandrum sativum.

Corncockle,
Lychnis githago.

Corn Crowfoot,
Ranunculus arvensis.

Cornflower,
Centaurea cyanus.

Corn Marigold,
Chrysanthemum segetum.

Corn Poppy,
Papaver rhœas.

Corn Salad,
Valerianella (the genus).

Corn Spurrey,
Spergula arvensis.

Corn Thistle,
Carduus arvensis.

Cornel,
Cornus sanguinea.

Cornish Heath,
Erica vagans.

Corpse Plant,
Monotropa uniflora.

Cotton Grass,
Eriophorum (the genus).

Cotton Thistle.
Onopordum acanthium.

Cotton Weed,
Gnaphalium (the genus), or Diotis maritima.

Couch Grass,
Triticum repens.

Cowbane,
Cicuta virosa.

Cowbell,
Silene inflata.

Cowberry,
Vaccinium vitis-idæa.

Cow Parsley,
Anthriscus sylvestris.

Cow Parsnip,
Heracleum (the genus).

Cowslip,
Primula veris.

Cow Vetch,
Vicia cracca.

Cow Wheat,
Melampyrum (the genus).

Crab,
Pyrus malus.

Crakeberry,
Empetrum nigrum.

Cranberry,
Vaccinium oxycoccos.

Crane's-bill,
Geranium (the genus).

Creeping Crowfoot,
Ranunculus repens.

Cross-wort,
Galium cruciatum.

Crowberry,
Empetrum nigrum.

Crowfoot,
Ranunculus (the genus).

Crowfoot Anemone,
Anemone ranunculoides.

Crow Garlic,
Allium vineale.

Crow's Foot,
Lotus corniculatus.

Cuckoo Flower,
Cardamine pratensis,
Orchis mascula, or Hya-
cinthus non-scriptus.

Cuckoo Grass,
Luzula campestris.

Cuckoo Pint,
Arum maculatum.

Cudweed,
Gnaphalium (the genus).

Currant,
Ribes (the genus).

Cursed Crowfoot,
Ranunculus sceleratus.

Cushion Pink,
Armeria maritima.

Cut Finger,
Vinca major.

Cut Grass,
Leersia oryzoides.

Cyphel,
Cherleria sedoides.

Daffodil,
Narcissus pseudo-narcissus.

Daisy,
Bellis perennis.

Dame's Violet,
Hesperis matronalis.

Dandelion,
Taraxacum officinale.

Dane's Flower,
Anemone pulsatilla.

Darnel,
Lolium temulentum.

Darning Needle,
Scandix pecten-veneris.

Dart Grass,
Holcus mollis.

Deadly Nightshade,
Atropa belladonna.

Dead Nettle,
Lamium (the genus).

Deptford Pink,
Dianthus armeria.

Devil's Bit,
Scabiosa succisa.

Dewberry,
Rubus cæsius.

Dirty Dick,
Chenopodium album.

Dittander,
Lepidium latifolium.

Dock,
Rumex (the genus).

Dodder,
Cuscuta (the genus).

Dog Rose,
Rosa canina.

Dog Thistle,
Carduus arvensis.

Dogwood,
Cornus sanguinea.

Dog's Mercury,
Mercurialis perennis.

Dog's Parsley,
Æthusa cynapium.

Dog's Tail Grass,
Cynosurus cristatus.

Dog's Tongue,
Cynoglossum officinale.

Dog's Tooth Grass,
Cynodon dactylon.

Dove's Foot,
Geranium molle.

Down Thistle,
Onopordum acanthium.

Drooping Avens,
Geum rivale.

Drooping Tulip,
Fritillaria meleagris.

Drop-wort,
Œnanthe crocata.

Duck Weed,
Lemna (the genus).

Dutch Clover,
Trifolium repens.

Dwale,
Atropa belladonna.

Dyer's Greenweed,
Genista tinctoria.

Dyer's Rocket,
Reseda luteola.

Earthnut,
Bunium flexuosum.

Earth Smoke,
Fumaria officinalis.

Easter Flower,
Anemone pulsatilla.

Eglantine,
Rosa rubiginosa.

Eggs and Bacon,
Linaria vulgaris, or Lotus
corniculatus.

Elder,
Sambucus nigra.

Elecampane,
Inula helenium.

Eleven o'clock Lady,
Ornithogalum umbellatum.

Elm,
Ulmus (the genus).

Enchanter's Nightshade,
Circæa lutetiana.

Erriff,
Galium aparine.

Eryngo,
Eryngium (the genus).

Espibawn,
Chrysanthemum leucan-
themum.

Euphrasy,
Euphrasia officinalis.

Evening Primrose,
Œnothera (the genus).

Everlasting,
Antennaria dioicum, or
Gnaphalium (the genus).

Everlasting Pea,
Lathyrus latifolia.

Eyebright,
Euphrasia officinalis.

Fair Maids of February,
Galanthus nivalis.

Fair Maids of France,
Achillea ptarmica.

Fair Maids of Kent,
Ranunculus aconitifolius.

Fairy Fingers,
Digitalis purpurea.

Fat Hen,
Chenopodium album.

Feather Foil,
Hottonia palustris.

Feather Grass,
Stipa pennata.

Felon Herb,
Artemisia vulgaris.

Felon-wort,
Solanum dulcamara.

Fenberry,
Vaccinium oxycoccos.

Fennel,
Fœniculum vulgare.

Fenugrec,
Trigonella ornithopo-
dioides.

Ferns,
Filices (the order).

Fescue Grass,
Festuca (the genus).

Feverfew,
Matricaria parthenium.

Fever-wort,
Erythræa centaurium.

Fiddle Dock,
Rumex pulcher.

Field Madder,
Sherardia arvensis.

Fig-wort,
Scrophularia (the genus), or
Ranunculus ficaria.

Filmy Fern,
Hymenophyllum (the genus).
Fingers and Thumbs,
Lotus corniculatus.
Fiorin Grass,
Agrostis alba.
Fir,
Pinus sylvestris.
Fire Weed,
Plantago media.
Fir Rape,
Monotropa hypopitys.
Five Leaf,
Potentilla reptans.
Flag,
Iris (the genus).
Flannel,
Verbascum thapsus.
Flax,
Linum usitatissimum.
Flax Seed,
Radiola millegrana.
Flax Weed,
Linaria vulgaris.
Flea Bane,
Erigeron (the genus).
Flea-wort,
Cineraria (the genus).
Fleur de lis,
Iris (the genus).
Flixweed,
Sisymbrium sophia.
Float Grass,
Glyceria fluitans.
Flower de Luce,
Iris (the genus).
Flowering Rush,
Butomus umbellatus.
Fluellin,
Linaria elatine.
Fly Orchis,
Ophrys muscifera.
Fool's Parsley,
Æthusa cynapium
Fool's Watercress,
Helosciadium nodiflorum.
Forget-me-not,
Myosotis (the genus).
Four-leaved Grass,
Paris quadrifolia.
Fowl Grass,
Poa trivialis.
Foxglove,
Digitalis purpurea.
Foxtail,
Alopecurus pratensis.
Fragrant Orchis,
Gymnadenia conopsea.
French Willow,
Epilobium angustifolium.

Friar's Cap,
Aconitum capellus.
Friar's Crown,
Carduus eriophorus.
Fritillary,
Fritillaria meleagris.
Frog-bit,
Hydrocharis morsus ranæ.
Fuller's Herb,
Saponaria officinalis.
Fume-wort,
Corydalis (the genus).
Fumitory,
Fumaria (the genus).
Furze,
Ulex (the genus).

Gale,
Myrica gale.
Galingale,
Cyperus longus.
Gang Flower,
Polygala vulgaris.
Garden-gate,
Viola tricolor.
Garlic,
Allium (the genus).
Garlic Sage,
Teucrium scorodonia.
Gatten,
Euonymus europæus, or Cornus sanguinea.
Gean,
Prunus avium.
Gentian,
Gentiana (the genus).
Germander,
Teucrium chamædrys.
Germander Speedwell,
Veronica chamædrys.
Gethsemane,
Orchis mascula.
Gill,
Nepeta glechoma.
Gillyflower,
Dianthus caryophyllus, Matthiola incana, or Cheiranthus cheiri.
Gipsy-wort,
Lycopus europæus.
Gladwyn,
Iris fœtidissima.
Glass-wort,
Salicornia herbacea.
Globe Flower,
Trollius (the genus).
Goatsbeard,
Tragopogon pratensis.
Gold Dust,
Sedum acre.
Gold of Pleasure,
Camelina sativa.

Golden Rod,
Solidago virgaurea.
Golden Tuft,
Alyssum saxatile.
Goldilocks,
Ranunculus auricomus, or Chrysocoma linosyris.
Goldings,
Chrysanthemum segetum.
Good King Henry,
Chenopodium bonus henricus.
Gooseberry,
Ribes grossularia.
Gooseberry Pie,
Epilobium hirsutum.
Goosebill,
Galium aparine.
Goosecorn,
Juncus squarrosus.
Goosefoot,
Chenopodium (the genus).
Goosegray,
Potentilla anserina.
Goose Tongue,
Achillea ptarmica.
Gorse,
Ulex (the genus).
Gout Ivy,
Ajuga chamæpitys.
Goutweed,
Ægopodium podagraria.
Gowan,
Bellis perennis, or any of the yellow Ranunculi.
Grace of God,
Hypericum calycinum.
Grasses,
Gramineæ (the order).
Grass of Parnassus,
Parnassia palustris.
Greeds,
Potamogeton (the genus).
Green Man,
Aceras anthropophora.
Green Sauce,
Rumex acetosella.
Grim the Collier,
Hieracium aurantiacum.
Gromwell,
Lithospermum (the genus).
Ground-well,
Veronica officinalis.
Ground Ivy,
Nepeta glechoma.
Ground Pine,
Ajuga chamæpitys.
Groundsel,
Senecio (the genus).
Guelder Rose,
Viburnum opulus.

Guimauve,
Althæa officinalis.

Guinea Hen,
Fritillaria meleagris.

Hair Bell,
Campanula rotundifolia.

Hallelujah,
Oxalis acetosella.

Hammer Sedge,
Cyperus hirta.

Hard Fern,
Blechnum boreale.

Hardock,
Arctium lappa.

Hare Bell,
Campanula rotundifolia.

Hare's Beard,
Verbascum thapsus.

Hare's Ear,
Bupleurum rotundifolium.

Hare's Eye,
Lychnis diurna.

Hare's Tail,
Lagurus ovatus.

Hare Thistle,
Sonchus oleraceus.

Harlock,
Arctium lappa.

Harriff,
Galium aparine.

Hart's Tongue,
Scolopendrium vulgare.

Hartwort,
Tordylium maximum.

Hassocks,
Carex paniculata.

Hautboy,
Fragaria elatior.

Hawkbit,
Leontodon (the genus).

Hawkweed,
Hieracium (the genus).

Hawksbeard,
Crepis (the genus).

Hawthorn,
Cratægus oxyacantha.

Hay Maids,
Nepeta glechoma.

Hazel,
Corylus avellana.

Headache,
Papaver rhœas.

Heartsease,
Viola tricolor.

Heath,
Erica (the genus).

Heather,
Calluna (the genus).

Hedgehog,
Ranunculus arvensis.

Hedge Hyssop,
Scutellaria minor.

Hedge Mustard,
Sisymbrium officinale.

Hedge Parsley,
Torilis anthriscus.

Hedge Vine,
Clematis vitalba.

Hellebore,
Helleborus (the genus).

Helleborine,
Epipactis (the genus) or Cephalanthera (the genus).

Hemlock,
Conium maculatum.

Hemp Agrimony,
Eupatorium cannabinum.

Hemp Nettle,
Galeopsis tetrahit.

Henbane,
Hyoscyamus niger.

Henbit,
Lamium amplexicaule, or Veronica hederifolia.

Hen Plant,
Plantago lanceolata.

Hen's Foot,
Caucalis daucoides.

Herb Bennet,
Geum urbanum, Conium maculatum, or Valeriana officinalis.

Herb Carpenter,
Prunella vulgaris.

Herb Christopher,
Actæa spicata, or Osmunda regalis.

Herb Gerard,
Ægopodium podagraria.

Herb Margaret,
Bellis perennis.

Herb Paris,
Paris quadrifolia.

Herb Peter,
Primula veris.

Herb Robert,
Geranium robertianum.

Herb Trinity,
Viola tricolor.

Herb Twopence,
Lysimachia nummularia.

Heron's Bill,
Erodium (the genus).

Herringbone Fern,
Blechnum boreale.

High Taper,
Verbascum thapsus.

Hindberry,
Rubus idæus.

Hind Heal,
Chenopodium botryoides and Teucrium scorodonia.

Hip Wort,
Cotyledon umbilicus.

Hoary Mullein,
Verbascum pulverulentum.

Hog Cherry,
Prunus padus.

Hog Nut,
Bunium flexuosum.

Hog's Fennel,
Peucedanum officinale.

Hog Weed,
Heracleum sphondylium.

Hole Wort,
Corydalis tuberosa, or Adoxa moschatellina.

Holly,
Ilex aquifolium.

Holly Fern,
Polystichum lonchitis.

Holy Ghost,
Angelica sylvestris.

Holy Grass,
Hierochloe borealis.

Holy Hay,
Medicago sativa.

Holy Herb,
Verbena officinalis.

Holy Rope,
Eupatorium cannabinum.

Holy Rose,
Andromeda polifolia.

Home Wort,
Sempervivum tectorum.

Hone Wort,
Trinia vulgaris.

Honeysuckle,
Lonicera periclymenum.

Honey Wort,
Sison amomum.

Hood Wort,
Scutellaria (the genus).

Hooded Grass,
Bromus mollis.

Hoofs,
Tussilago farfara.

Hookheal,
Prunella vulgaris.

Hop,
Humulus lupulus.

Hop Clover,
Trifolium procumbens, or Medicago lupulina.

Hopes,
Matthiola incana.

Horehound,
Ballota nigra, or Marrubium vulgare.

Hornbeam,
Carpinus betulus.

Hornwort,
Ceratophyllum demersum.

Horned Pondweed,
Zannichellia (the genus).

Horned Poppy,
Glaucium luteum.

Horned Rampion,
Phyteuma (the genus).

Horsebane,
Œnanthe phellandrium.

Horse Elder,
Inula helenium.

Horse Mint,
Mentha sylvestris.

Horse Parsley,
Smyrnium olusatrum.

Horse Radish,
Cochlearia armoracia.

Horse Shoe Vetch,
Hippocrepis comosa.

Horsetail,
Equisetum (the genus).

Horse Thyme,
Calamintha clinopodium.

Horse Tongue,
Scolopendrium vulgare.

Hound's Berry,
Cornus sanguinea.

Hound's Tongue,
Cynoglossum officinalis.

Houseleek,
Sempervivum (the genus).

Hove,
Nepeta glechoma.

Huckleberry,
Vaccinium myrtillus.

Hulver,
Ilex aquifolium.

Hundredfold,
Galium verum.

Hunger Weed,
Ranunculus acris.

Hurtleberry,
Vaccinium myrtillus.

Hurts,
Vaccinium myrtillus.

Hurt Sickle,
Centaurea cyanus.

Hyacinth,
Hyacinthus nonscriptus.

Imbreke,
Sempervivum tectorum.

Indian Eye,
Dianthus plumarius.

Indian Moss,
Saxifraga hypnoides.

Iron Grass,
Polygonum aviculare.

Iron Head,
Centaurea nigra.

Ivy,
Hedera helix.

Ivy-wort,
Linaria cymbalaria.

Jack by the Hedge,
Sisymbrium alliaria.

Jack-go-to-bed-at-noon,
Ornithogalum umbellatum,
or Tragopogon pratensis.

Jack of the Buttery,
Sedum acre.

Jacob's Ladder,
Polemonium cœruleum.

Jacoby,
Senecio jacobæa.

Jerusalem Cowslip,
Pulmonaria officinalis.

Jerusalem Oak,
Teucrium botryoides.

Jerusalem Star,
Tragopogon porrifolius.

Jew's Myrtle,
Ruscus aculeatus.

Joint Vetch,
Arthrolobium (the genus).

Joseph's Flower,
Tragopogon pratensis.

Juniper,
Juniperus communis.

Juno's Tears,
Verbena officinalis.

Jupiter's Beard,
Sempervivum tectorum.

Jur Nut,
Bunium flexuosum.

Kale,
Brassica oleracea.

Kecks,
Æthusa cynapium.

Kemps,
Plantago media.

Kendal Green,
Genista tinctoria.

Kentish Balsam,
Mercurialis perennis.

Kettle Dock,
Rumex obtusifolius.

Kidney Vetch,
Anthyllis vulneraria.

Kidney Wort,
Cotyledon umbilicus.

Kingcup,
Ranunculis acris.

King Fern,
Osmunda regalis.

King's Clover,
Melilotus officinalis.

Kinnikinnick,
Arctostaphylos uva ursi.

Knapweed,
Centaurea nigra.

Knapwell,
Scleranthus annuus.

Knawel,
Scleranthus (the genus).

Knee Holly,
Ruscus aculeatus.

Knipper Nut,
Vicia orobus.

Knob Sedge,
Sparganium ramosum.

Knot Berry,
Rubus chamæmorus.

Knot Grass,
Illecebrum (the genus).

Lady Fern,
Athyrium filix-fœmina.

Lady of the Meadow,
Spiræa ulmaria.

Lady's Bower,
Clematis vitalba.

Lady's Finger,
Anthyllis vulneraria.

Lady's Glove,
Inula conyza.

Lady's Hair,
Briza media.

Lady's Mantle,
Alchemilla vulgaris.

Lady's Nightcap,
Convolvulus sepium.

Lady's Pincushion,
Armeria maritima.

Lady's Seal,
Tamus communis.

Lady's Slipper,
Cypripedium (the genus).

Lady's Smock,
Cardamine pratensis.

Lady's Thimble,
Campanula rotundifolia.

Lady's Thistle,
Carduus marianus.

Lady's Thumb,
Polygonum persicaria.

Lady's Tresses,
Spiranthes (the genus).

Lake Weed,
Polygonum hydropiper.

Lamb-in-a-Pulpit,
Arum maculatum.

Lamb's Cress,
Cardamine hirsuta.

Lamb's Ear,
Stachys germanica.

Lamb's Lettuce,
Valerianella olitoria.

Lamb's Toe,
Lotus corniculatus.

Lamb's Tongue,
Plantago media.

Lamp Flower,
Lychnis (the genus).

Land Whin,
Ononis arvensis.

Larkspur,
Delphinium (the genus).

Lavender Thrift,
Statice limonium.

Leek,
Allium ampeloprasum.

Lent Lily,
Narcissus pseudo-narcissus.

Leopard's Bane,
Doronicum (the genus) or
Paris quadrifolia.

Lettuce,
Lactuca (the genus).

Lily,
Lilium (the genus).

Lily of the Mountain,
Polygonatum multiflorum.

Lily of the Valley,
Convallaria majalis.

Lily Grass,
Butomus umbellatus.

Lime,
Tilia europæa.

Lime-wort,
Lychnis viscaria.

Linden,
Tilia europæa.

Ling,
Calluna vulgaris.

Ling Berry,
Empetrum nigrum, or
Vaccinium vitis-idæa.

Lion's Foot,
Alchemilla vulgaris.

Lion's Mouth,
Linaria vulgaris, or
Antirrhinum (the genus).

Lion's Snap,
Lamium amplexicaule.

Lion's Tooth,
Leontodon, (the genus).

Liquorice,
Astragalus glyciphyllos.

Lithy,
Viburnum lantana.

Livelong,
Sedum telephium.

Lizard,
Orchis hircina.

Lob Grass,
Bromus mollis.

Loddon Lily,
Leucojum æstivum.

Lode-wort,
Ranunculus aquatilis.

Logger-heads,
Centaurea (the genus).

London Pride,
Saxifraga umbrosa.

London Rocket,
Sisymbrium irio.

Long Purple,
Orchis mascula.

Loosestrife,
Lysimachia (the genus) or
Lythrum salicaria.

Lords and Ladies,
Arum maculatum.

Lot,
Pyrus aria.

Louse-wort,
Pedicularis (the genus).

Lovage,
Ligusticum scoticum.

Love-in-Idleness,
Viola tricolor.

Loveman,
Galium aparine.

Lucerne,
Medicago sativa.

Lucken Gowan,
Trollius europæus.

Lunary,
Botrychium lunaria.

Lung-wort,
Pulmonaria (the genus).

Lyme Grass,
Elymus arenarius.

Mackerel Mint,
Mentha viridis.

Madder,
Rubia (the genus) or
Sherardia (the genus).

Mad-wort,
Asperugo procumbens, or
Alyssum (the genus).

Maidenhair,
Adiantum capillus veneris,
Asplenium trichomanes,
or Narthecium ossi-
fragum.

Maid of the Meadow,
Spiræa ulmaria.

Maiden Pink,
Dianthus deltoides.

Maiden's Honesty,
Clematis vitalba.

Maid's Hair,
Galium verum.

Male Fern,
Lastræa filix mas.

Mallow,
Malva (the genus), Althæa
(the genus), or Lavatera
arborea.

Mandrake,
Bryonia dioica.

Manna Grass,
Glyceria fluitans.

Man Orchis,
Aceras anthropophora.

Maple,
Acer (the genus).

Mare's Tail,
Hippuris (the genus).

Marguerite,
Chrysanthemum leucan-
themum.

Marigold,
Chrysanthemum segetum.

Marjoram,
Origanum (the genus).

Marram,
Ammophila arundinacea.

Marsh Beetle,
Typha latifolia.

Marsh Cinquefoil,
Comarum palustre.

Marsh Elder,
Viburnum opulus.

Marsh Fern,
Lastræa thelypteris.

Marsh Mallow,
Althæa (the genus).

Marsh Marigold,
Caltha palustris.

Marsh Parsley,
Apium graveolens.

Marsh Pennywort,
Hydrocotyle vulgaris.

Marsh Trefoil,
Menyanthes trifoliata.

Mary Bud,
Caltha palustris.

Mary's Gold,
Caltha palustris.

Mastel Tree,
Acer campestre.

Master-wort,
Peucedanum ostruthium.

Matfellon,
Centaurea nigra, or C.
scabiosa.

Mat Grass,
Nardus stricta.

Mathes,
Anthemis cotula.

Maudlin Wort,
Chrysanthemum leucan-
themum.

Mawseed,
Papaver somniferum.

May,
Cratægus oxyacantha.

Mayblobs,
Caltha palustris.

Mayflower,
Cardamine pratensis.

Maylily,
Convallaria majalis.

Mayweed,
Anthemis cotula.

Mazard,
Prunus avium.

Meadow Bright,
Caltha palustris.

Meadow Cress,
Cardamine pratensis.

Meadow Grass,
Poa (the genus), or
Schlerochloa (the genus).

Meadow Nut,
Comarum palustre.

Meadow Parsnip,
Heracleum sphondylium.

Meadow Pink,
Lychnis flos-cuculi.

Meadow Rocket,
Orchis latifolia.

Meadow Rout,
Caltha palustris.

Meadow Rue,
Thalictrum (the genus).

Meadow Saffron,
Colchicum autumnale.

Meadow Saxifrage,
Silaus pratensis.

Meadow Sweet,
Spiræa ulmaria.

Mealy Tree,
Viburnum lantana.

Medick,
Medicago (the genus).

Medlar,
Mespilus (the genus).

Melic Grass,
Melica (the genus).

Melilot,
Melilotus (the genus), or
Medicago lupulina.

Mercury,
Mercurialis perennis.

Mew,
Meum athamanticum.

Mezereon,
Daphne mezereum.

Michaelmas Daisy,
Aster tripolium.

Midsummer Daisy,
Chrysanthemum leucan-
themum.

Midsummer Men,
Sedum telephium.

Mignonette,
Reseda luteola.

Milfoil,
Achillea (the genus).

Milk Gowan,
Taraxacum officinale.

Milk Grass,
Valerianella olitoria.

Milk Thistle,
Carduus marianus.

Milk Vetch,
Astragalus (the genus).

Milk Weed,
Peucedanum   palustre,
Sonchus oleraceus, or
Polygala (the genus).

Milk Wort,
Polygala (the genus).

Miller's Star,
Stellaria holostea.

Millet Grass,
Milium (the genus).

Mint,
Mentha (the genus).

Mistletoe,
Viscum album.

Mithridate Mustard,
Thlaspi arvense.

Mitre flower,
Cyclamen (the genus).

Modesty,
Bupleurum rotundifolium.

Moneywort,
Lysimachia nummularia.

Monkey Flower,
Mimulus (the genus).

Monkshood,
Aconitum napellus.

Monk's Rhubarb,
Rumex alpinus.

Monox,
Empetrum nigrum.

Moon Daisy,
Chrysanthemum leucan-
themum.

Moonwort,
Botrychium lunaria.

Moorberry,
Vaccinium oxycoccos.

Moor Grass,
Sesleria cœrulea.

Moor Heath,
Erica vagans.

Moor Myrtle,
Myrica gale.

Moor Whin,
Genista anglica.

Moorwort,
Andromeda polifolia.

Morel,
Atropa belladonna.

Mortal,
Solanum dulcamara.

Moschatel,
Adoxa moschatellina.

Moss Campion,
Silene acaulis

Moss Rush,
Juncus squarrosus

Mossy-red-shanks,
Tillæa muscosa.

Moth Mullein,
Verbascum blattaria.

Mother of Thousands,
Linaria cymbalaria.

Mother of Thyme,
Thymus serpyllum.

Mother of Wheat,
Veronica hederæfolia.

Mother's Heart,
Capsella bursa pastoris.

Motherwort,
Leonurus cardiaca.

Mountain Anemone,
Anemone apennina.

Mountain Ash,
Pyrus aucuparia.

Mountain Fern,
Lastræa oreopteris.

Mountain Sage,
Teucrium scorodonia.

Mountain Sorrel,
Oxyria reniformis.

Mourning Widow,
Geranium phæum.

Mouse Ear,
Hieracium pilosella, Ceras-
tium (the genus), or
Myosotis (the genus).

Mouse tail,
Myosurus minimus.

Muckweed,
Chenopodium album.

Mudwort,
Limosella aquatica.

Mugget,
Convallaria majalis.

Mugwort,
Galium cruciatum, or Artemisia vulgaris.

Mullein,
Verbascum (the genus).

Mullet,
Inula dysenterica.

Munshock,
Vaccinium vitis-idæa.

Musk Mallow,
Malva moschata.

Musk Orchis,
Herminium monorchis,

Musk Thistle,
Carduus nutans

Mustard,
Sinapis (the genus).

Mutton Chops,
Galium aparine.

Myrrh,
Myrrhis odorata.

Myrtle Flag,
Acorus calamus

Myrtle Spurge,
Euphorbia lathyris.

Nailwort,
Draba verna.

Naked Ladies,
Colchicum autumnale.

Nap at Noon,
Tragopogon pratensis.

Naughty Man's Cherry,
Atropa belladonna.

Navelwort,
Cotyledon umbilicus.

Navew,
Brassica campestris.

Needle Chervil,
Scandix pecten veneris.

Needle Whin,
Genista anglica.

Neele,
Lolium temulentum.

Nettle,
Urtica (the genus).

Nightingale,
Geranium robertianum.

Nightshade,
Solanum (the genus), also
Atropa belladonna.

Ninety Knot,
Polygonum aviculare.

Nipplewort,
Lapsana (the genus) or
Arnoseris (the genus).

Nit Grass,
Gastridium lendigerum.

None so Pretty,
Saxifraga umbrosa.

Nonsuch,
Medicago lupulina.

Noontide,
Tragopogon pratense.

Noops,
Rubus chamæmorus.

Nose Bleed,
Achillea millefolium.

Nottingham Catchfly,
Silene nutans.

Nutbush,
Corylus avellana.

Oak.
Quercus (the genus).

Oak of Paradise,
Chenopodium botryoides.

Oak Fern,
Polypodium dryopteris.

Oat,
Avena (the genus).

Ofbit,
Scabiosa succisa.

Old Man's Beard,
Clematis vitalba.

Old Woman,
Artemisia absinthium.

One Berry,
Paris quadrifolia.

Orache,
Atriplex (the genus).

Orpine,
Sedum telephium.

Osier,
Salix viminalis.

Osterick,
Polygonum bistorta.

Oxberry,
Tamus communis.

Ox-eye,
Chrysanthemum leucanthemum.

Ox-heel,
Helleborus fœtidus.

Ox-lip,
Primula elatior.

Ox-tongue,
Helminthia echioides.

Padelion,
Alchemilla vulgaris.

Paigle,
Primula veris.

Palm,
Salix caprea.

Pansy,
Viola tricolor.

Parsley,
Petroselinum (the genus).

Parsley Fern,
Allosorus crispus.

Parsley Piert,
Alchemilla arvensis.

Parsnip,
Pastinaca (the genus).

Pasque Flower,
Anemone pulsatilla.

Passerage,
Lepidium campestre.

Pear,
Pyrus communis.

Pearlwort,
Sagina (the genus).

Pellitory of the Wall,
Parietaria (the genus).

Penny Cress,
Thlaspi arvense.

Penny Rot,
Hydrocotyle vulgaris.

Penny Royal.
Mentha pulegium.

Penny-wort,
Linaria cymbalaria.

Peppermint.
Mentha piperita.

Pepperwort,
Lepidium latifolium.

Periwinkle,
Vinca (the genus).

Pestilence Weed,
Petasites vulgaris.

Pettigrew,
Ruscus aculeatus.

Petty Whin,
Genista anglica.

Pheasant's Eye,
Adonis autumnalis.

Picotee,
Dianthus caryophyllus.

Pigeon's Foot,
Geranium columbinum.

Pig Nut,
Bunium flexuosum.

Pilewort,
Ranunculus ficaria.

Pillwort,
Pilularia globulifera.

Pimpernel,
Anagallis arvensis, Pimpinella saxifraga, Poterium
sanguisorba or Prunella
vulgaris.

Pine Sap,
Monotropa hypopitys.

Pink,
Dianthus (the genus).

Pink Weed,
Polygonum aviculare.

Pipe-wort,
Eriocaulon septangulare.

Plague Flower,
Petasites vulgaris.

Plantain,
Plantago (the genus).

Ploughman's Spikenard,
Inula conyza.

Polypody,
Polypodium (the genus).

Pondweed,
Potamogeton (the genus).

Pondwort,
Stratiotes aloides.

Poor Man's Parmacetie,
Capsella bursa-pastoris.

Poor Man's Rhubarb,
Thalictrum flavum.

Poor Man's Weather-glass,
Anagallis arvensis.

Poplar,
Populus (the genus).

Poppy,
Papaver (the genus).

Portland Arrowroot,
Arum maculatum.

Prattling Parnell,
Saxifraga geum.

Pricket,
Sedum acre.

Prickwood,
Cornus sanguinea, or
Euonymus europæus.

Priest's Crown,
Taraxacum officinale.

Primrose,
Primula acaulis.

Privet,
Ligustrum (the genus).

Procession Flower,
Polygala vulgaris.

Purification Flower,
Galanthus nivalis.

Purslane,
Portulaca (the genus).

Quaking Grass,
Briza media.

Queen of the Meadow,
Spiræa salicifolia, or S.
ulmaria.

Quicken,
Pyrus aucuparia.

Quill Wort,
Isoetes (the genus).

Radish,
Raphanus (the genus).

Ragged Robin,
Lychnis floscuculi.

Ragwort,
Senecio (the genus).

Rampe,
Arum maculatum.

Rampion,
Campanula rapunculus, or
Phyteuma (the genus).

Ram's Horns,
Orchis mascula.

Ramsons,
Allium ursinum.

Rape,
Brassica napus.

Raspberry,
Rubus idæus.

Rattle Box,
Rhinanthus cristagalli.

Red Legs,
Polygonum bistorta.

Red Maithes,
Adonis autumnalis.

Red Morocco,
Adonis autumnalis.

Red Rattle,
Pedicularis sylvatica.

Red Rot,
Drosera rotundifolia.

Red Shanks,
Polygonum persicaria.

Reed,
Arundo (the genus).

Reed Mace,
Typha latifolia.

Rest Harrow,
Ononis (the genus).

Rib Grass,
Plantago lanceolata.

Roast Beef,
Iris fœtidissima.

Rocambole,
Allium scorodoprasum.

Rock Brake,
Allosorus crispus.

Rock Cress,
Arabis (the genus).

Rocket,
Reseda lutea, Sisymbrium
irio, Cakile maritima, or
Diplotaxis tenuifolia.

Rockrose,
Cistus (the genus).

Rogation Flower,
Polygala vulgaris.

Rose,
Rosa (the genus).

Rosebay,
Epilobium angustifolium.

Rose Elder,
Viburnum opulus.

Rowan,
Pyrus aucuparia.

Rupture-wort,
Herniaria glabra.

Rush,
Juncus (the genus).

Rye Grass,
Lolium (the genus).

Sage,
Salvia (the genus).

Sainfoin,
Onobrychis sativa.

Saint Anthony's Nut,
Bunium flexuosum.

Saint Barbara's Cress,
Barbarea vulgaris.

Saint Barnaby's Thistle,
Centaurea solstitialis.

Saint Dabeoc's Heath,
Menziesia polifolia.

Saint James's Wort,
Capsella bursa pastoris, or
Senecio jacobæa.

Saint John's Wort,
Hypericum (the genus).

Saint Patrick's Cabbage,
Saxifraga umbrosa.

Saint Peter's Wort,
Crithmum maritimum,
Primula veris, or Hyperi-
cum quadrangulum.

Sallow,
Salix (the genus).

Sallow Thorn,
Hippophae rhamnoides.

Salsify,
Tragopogon porrifolius.

Saltwort,
Glaux maritima.

Samphire,
Crithmum maritimum.

Sandwort,
Arenaria (the genus).

Sanguinary,
Achillea millefolium.

Sanicle,
Sanicula europæa.

Saucealone,
Erysimum alliaria.

Satin Flower,
Stellaria holostea.

Saw-wort,
Serratula (the genus).

Saxifrage,
Saxifraga (the genus).

Scabious,
Scabiosa (the genus).

Scotch Asphodel,
Tofieldia palustris.

Scotch Fir,
Pinus sylvestris.

Scotch Thistle,
Onopordum acanthium.

Scurvy Grass,
Cochlearia (the genus).

Sea Beet,
Beta maritima.

Sea Blite,
Suæda maritima.

Sea Buckthorn,
Hippophae rhamnoides.

Sea Hay,
Zostera marina.

Sea Heath,
Frankenia lævis.

Sea Holly,
Eryngium maritimum.

Sea Kale,
Crambe maritima.

Sea Lavender,
Statice limonium.

Sea Pink,
Armeria maritima.

Sea Poppy,
Glaucium luteum.

Sea Purslane,
Obione (the genus)

Sea Rocket,
Cakile maritima.

Seave,
Juncus (the genus).

Sedge,
Carex (the genus).

Self-heal,
Prunella vulgaris.

Service Tree,
Pyrus torminalis.

Setter Wort,
Helleborus fœtidus.

Shamrock,
Oxalis acetosella., Medicago lupulina, or Trifolium repens.

Shamrock, Four-leaved,
Trifolium repens var. purpureum.

Share Wort,
Aster tripolium.

Sheep's Bane,
Hydrocotyle vulgaris.

Sheep's Bit,
Jasione (the genus).

Sheep's Sorrel,
Rumex acetosella.

Shepherd's Club,
Verbascum thapsus.

Shepherd's Cress,
Teesdalia nudicaulis.

Shepherd's Needle,
Scandix pecten veneris.

Shepherd's Purse,
Capsella bursa pastoris.

Shepherd's Rod,
Dipsacus (the genus).

Shore Weed,
Littorella lacustris.

Silver Weed,
Potentilla anserina.

Simson,
Senecio vulgaris.

Skull Cap,
Scutellaria (the genus).

Sloe,
Prunus spinosa.

Smallage,
Apium graveolens.

Small Reed,
Calamagrostis (the genus).

Smoke Wood,
Clematis vitalba.

Snake's Head,
Fritillaria meleagris.

Snakeweed,
Polygonum bistorta.

Snapdragon,
Antirrhinum (the genus).

Sneeze Wort,
Achillea ptармica.

Snowball,
Viburnum opulus.

Snowdrop,
Galanthus nivalis.

Snowflake,
Leucojum (the genus).

Soapwort,
Saponaria (the genus).

Soldier Orchis,
Orchis militaris.

Solomon's Seal.
Polygonatum (the genus).

Sorrel,
Oxalis (the genus), Rumex acetosella, or Oxyria reniformis.

Southernwood,
Artemisia campestris.

Sowbane,
Chenopodium rubrum.

Sow Thistle,
Sonchus (the genus), or Mulgedium alpinum.

Sparrow Tongue,
Polygonum aviculare.

Spearwort,
Ranunculus lingua, or R. flammula.

Speedwell,
Veronica (the genus).

Spider Orchis,
Orchis aranifera.

Spignel,
Meum athamanticum.

Spindle Tree,
Euonymus europæus.

Spleenwort,
Asplenium (the genus).

Spoonwort,
Cochlearia (the genus).

Spurge,
Euphorbia (the genus).

Spurge Laurel,
Daphne laureola.

Spurrey,
Spergula (the genus).

Squill,
Scilla (the genus).

Squinancy Wort,
Asperula cynanchica.

Squirrel Tail Grass,
Hordeum maritimum.

Staggerwort,
Senecio jacobæa.

Stanmarch,
Smyrnium olusatrum.

Star Fruit,
Actinocarpus damasonium.

Star of Bethlehem,
Ornithogalum umbellatum.

Star of Jerusalem,
Tragopogon porrifolius.

Star of the Earth,
Plantago coronopus.

Star of the Sea,
Aster tripolium.

Star Thistle,
Centaurea calcitrapa

Star-wort,
Callitriche (the genus).

Sticklewort,
Agrimonia eupatoria.

Stitchwort,
Stellaria (the genus).

Stonecrop,
Sedum (the genus).

Stork's Bill,
Erodium (the genus).

Strapwort,
Corrigiola littoralis.

Strawberry,
Fragaria vesca.

Strawberry Tree,
Arbutus unedo.

Succory,
Cichorium intybus.

Sulphur Weed,
Peucedanum officinale.

Sulphur Wort,
Œnanthe silaifolia.

Sundew,
Drosera (the genus).

Sunrose,
Helianthemum (the genus).

Sweetbriar,
Rosa rubiginosa.

Sweet Flag,
Acorus calamus.

Swine's Cress,
Coronopus (the genus).

Sword Lily,
Gladiolus (the genus).

Sycamore,
Acer pseudoplatanus.

Syndaw,
Alchemilla vulgaris.

Tamarisk,
Tamarix anglica.

Tansy,
Tanacetum vulgare.

Tare,
Vicia hirsuta.

Tassel Grass,
Ruppia maritima.

Teasel,
Dipsacus (the genus).

Thistle,
Carduus (the genus), Centaurea (the genus), Sonchus (the genus), Carlina (the genus), or Onopordum (the genus).

Thorough Wax,
Bupleurum rotundifolium.

Thrift,
Armeria maritima.

Throatwort,
Campanula latifolia.

Thyme,
Thymus serpyllum.

Timothy,
Phleum (the genus).

Tine Tare,
Vicia hirsuta.

Toadflax,
Linaria (the genus).

Toad Pipe,
Equisetum (the genus).

Toothwort,
Lathrea squamosa.

Torch,
Verbascum thapsus.

Tormentil,
Potentilla tormentilla.

Touch-me-not,
Impatiens noli-me-tangere.

Tower Mustard,
Turritis (the genus).

Toywort, .
Capsella bursa pasteris.

Traveller's Joy,
Clematis vitalba.

Treacle Mustard,
Erysimum (the genus).

Tree Mallow,
Lavatera arborea.

Trefoil,
Trifolium (the genus).

Tripoly,
Aster tripolium.

Troll Flower,
Trollius europæus.

Truelove,
Paris quadrifolia.

Tulip,
Tulipa sylvestris.

Turnip,
Brassica rapa.

Tutsan,
Hypericum androsæmum.

Tway Blade,
Listera ovata.

Twopenny Grass,
Lysimachia nummularia.

Upstart,
Colchicum autumnale.

Valerian,
Valeriana (the genus), or Centranthus ruber.

Velvet Leaf,
Lavatera arborea.

Venus Comb,
Scandix pecten veneris.

Vervain,
Verbena officinalis.

Vetch,
Vicia (the genus).

Vetchling,
Lathyrus (the genus).

Violet,
Viola (the genus).

Viper's Bugloss,
Echium vulgare.

Virgin's Bower,
Clematis vitalba.

Wagwant,
Briza media.

Wake Robin,
Arum maculatum.

Wallflower,
Cheiranthus cheiri.

Wall Pepper,
Sedum acre.

Wall Rue,
Asplenium ruta-muraria.

Wart Cress,
Coronopus (the genus).

Water Blob,
Caltha palustris.

Water Caltrops,
Caltha palustris.

Water Can,
Nuphar lutea.

Water Cress,
Nasturtium officinale.

Water Crowfoot,
Ranunculus aquatiiis.

Water Lily,
Nymphæa (the genus), or Nuphar (the genus).

Water Parsnip,
Sium latifolium.

Water Plantain,
Alisma plantago.

Water Soldier,
Stratiotes aloides.

Water Violet,
Hottonia palustris.

Waterwort,
Elatine (the genus).

Way Bennet,
Hordeum murinum.

Wayfaring Tree,
Viburnum lantana.

Waythorn,
Rhamnus catharticus.

Weasel Snout,
Lamium galeobdolon.

Welsh Poppy,
Meconopsis cambrica.

Wheat Grass,
Triticum caninum.

Whin,
Ulex (the genus), or Genista (the genus).

Whip Tongue,
Galium mollugo.

Whitebeam,
Pyrus aria.

White Bottle,
Silene inflata.

White Thorn,
Cratægus oxyacantha.

Whitlow Grass,
Draba (the genus).

Whorl Grass,
Catabrosa aquatica.

Whortleberry,
Vaccinium (the genus).

Wild William,
Lychnis flos-cuculi.

Willow,
Salix (the genus).

Willow Herb,
Epilobium (the genus).

Willow Thorn,
Hippophae rhamnoides.

Willow Weed,
Lythrum salicaria.

Wimberry,
Vaccinium myrtillus.

Wind Flower,
Anemone (the genus).

Winter Aconite,
Eranthis hyemalis.

Winter Cress,
Barbarea præcox.

Winter Green,
Pyrola (the genus) or Trientalis europæa.

Witch's Thimble,
Silene maritima

Woad,
Isatis tinctoria.

Woad Waxen,
Genista tinctoria.

Wolf's Bane,
Aconitum napellus.

Woodbine,
Lonicera periclymenum, Solanum dulcamara, or Convolvulus sepium.

Wood Crowfoot,
Ranunculus auricomus, or Anemone nemorosa.

Wood Lily,
Convallaria majalis.

Woodruff,
Asperula odorata.

Wood Rush,
Luzula (the genus).

Wood Sorrel,
Oxalis (the genus).

Wood Vine,
Clematis vitalba.

Woody Nightshade,
Solanum dulcamara.

Wormseed,
Erysimum cheiranthoides.

Wormwood,
Artemisia (the genus).

Woundwort,
Stachys germanica, or
Anthyllis vulneraria.

Wrack,
Zostera marina.

Wych Elm,
Ulmus montana.

Yarr,
Spergula arvensis.

Yarrow,
Achillea millefolium.

Yellow Cress,
Nasturtium palustre.

Yellow Rattle,
Rhinanthus cristagalli.

Yellow Wort,
Chlora perfoliata.

Yevering Bells,
Pyrola secunda.

Yew,
Taxus baccata.

Yorkshire Fog
Holcus lanatus.

Yorkshire Sanicle
Pinguicula vulgaris.

Zigzag Clover,
Trifolium medium

515.

CHAPTER II.

CLASSIFICATION.

WE wish to have a nodding acquaintance with the wild flowers we meet with, to be improved into intimacy if we think fit. Not a wish to be ashamed of, surely! How many of us are there who would find the world more interesting if we only knew the names of the flowers of the field, and the stars of the sky, and gave a thought to the things around us? How many—but let us to work, and moralise afterwards.

Here is a plant dug up by the ditcher and thrown on the footpath. What is its name? The plant is common enough, but we have never troubled to ascertain how it is distinguished from its fellows. Let us do so now. Here it is, root and all. Let us describe it not too technically, but just technically enough.

There is first its *fibrous* root. From the root rises the *stem*. The stem is slender, and is lightly clothed with hairs. It is *simple*; had it been branched at all it would have been *compound*; had the branches been two in number and fairly equal in length, it would have been *forked*. It is perpendicular or *erect*. Had it been horizontal when it left the root and then turned upward it would have been *ascending*; had it trailed along the ground it would have been *prostrate*; had it sent out roots from its joints as it trailed it would have been *creeping*.

From the stem spring the leaf-stalks or *petioles*, and these bear the deeply divided leaves. Had the leaves been directly joined on to the stem they would have been *sessile*. Deeply cut as the leaves are, they are not quite split into separate leaflets, and so they are *simple*; had they been completely separated they would have been *compound*, and then if they had three leaflets on a stalk they would be *ternate*, if five leaflets *quinate*, if more than five *pinnate* or feather-like. The divisions of the simple leaf are termed *lobes*, and the lobes here are uneven in number. There is one at the point and one or two or three on each side. When the lobes are narrow, and five or more in number, the leaf is *palmate*; when they are cut back equally down the midrib it is *pinnatifid*. The petiole is attached to the base of the leaf. Had the attachment been at its centre the leaf would have been *peltate* or buckler-shaped; had the stem passed through it the leaf would have been *perfoliate*; had each pair of leaves been united at their bases they would have been *connate*. The edge of the leaf is toothed or jagged; had its outline been unbroken it would have been *entire*. From the stem there also springs the flower stalk or *peduncle*, and the peduncle in this case is smooth and cylindrical.

The blossom consists of three rings. First we have a ring of small green leaves. These are the *sepals*, five in number ; the ring they form is the *calyx* or cup. The next ring is the bright yellow one of five delicate leaves. These are the *petals*, and the ring is called the *corolla* or little crown. Each petal tapers to a point ; the broad part is the *limb*, the pointed part the *claw.* At the claw or· *base* is a small scale covering the *nectary*, and in the nectary is a drop of honey. The petals are separate one from the other. Had they been united the broad part would have coalesced into the *border*, the claws into the *tube.* Having stripped off calyx and corolla, which together form the *perianth*, we come to the flower proper—the essential parts, or *reproductive organs.* First we have a ring of hair-like *filaments* springing from a centre cushion and each bearing its *anther.* Had there been no filament the anthers would have been *sessile.* These anthers contain the yellow fertilizing dust called *pollen.* In the centre we have the female portion of the flower, the *pistil* or *ovary*, consisting of several *carpels* or unripe fruitlets. Each carpel contains a single *ovule*, and will eventually develope into fruit when the pollen has been deposited upon it. Here are the remains of another bloom, one that has done its work, in which the ovary has been impregnated, the fruit has ripened, and the soft single-seeded carpel has become a hard, beaked, *achene.*

To what order does this plant belong ?

But what is an "order"? An order is a group of genera, as a "genus" is a group of species. What is a "species"? Species is the collective term for a group of individuals possessing similar characters which remain constant so long as the conditions of existence remain unchanged.

It was Linnæus to whom we owe the modern system of nomenclature, in which every species has a particular name compounded of a substantive and an adjective, whereof the former indicates the genus and the latter the species. In his day Latin was the general language of science ; in Latin his names were given ; and in Latin it is best they should remain until the English tongue has become universal, or the same plant is known by the same name in all English-speaking lands. In order to avoid a difficulty in distinguishing between generic and specific names, we have throughout in this book spelt the specific names without a capital letter. For the employment of the capital in proper adjectives there never was an excuse, the practice having been gradually adopted in ignorance of classical usages ; but in the case of the few genitives we are fully aware that the convenience of the student is our only defence.

By systematic botanists the characters of the genera are chiefly based on the forms of the flowers and fruit, while the characters of the species are furnished by all parts of the plant. But as our object is not a complete treatise on botany dealing with all the genera of the two hundred and odd orders into which the flowering plants of the world are divided, but merely to help the ordinary wayfarer to recognise his native flowers, without leading him away from the beaten track, we have confined ourselves to a series of diagnoses in which we have chosen whatever portion of the plant affords the readiest means of identification ; and we have used stems, leaves

C

flowers and fruit indiscriminately, so long as they are sufficient to
clearly distinguish between either species and species, genus and
genus, or even order and order.

For the proper identification of a plant it is important that it should
be in flower and fruit—in fact, that it should be complete in all its
parts ; and as all plants have not the convenient habit of being in full
leafage and in flower and fruit all at the same time, it would be
necessary that several specimens should be procured in different
stages of growth, were not some such general characters as are herein
given ordinarily enough for determination. It will be noted, however,
that it is with our country's flowers, and not our country's plants, that
we profess to deal; and that, after all, is the natural way, as the only
true basis of classification in the organic world must be the organs of
reproduction.

A few of the Linnæan descriptive terms, referring to these organs,
may here be recalled to the reader's recollection. When the stamens
and pistils are combined in the same flower, the flower is said to be
perfect; when they are in different flowers on the same plant, the
plant is said to be *monœcious;* when they are in different flowers on
different plants, the plant is said to be *diœcious.* When the stamens
and pistil are united in a column, the flower is *gynandrous;* when
the stamens are united by their anthers, the anthers are said to be
syngenesious; when they are united by the filaments in more than
two bundles, they are *polyadelphous;* when they are united in two
bundles, they are *diadelphous;* when they are united in a single bundle,
they are *monadelphous;* when they are of different lengths, with
four long and two short, they are *tetradynamous;* when there are two
long and two short, they are *didynamous.* It was chiefly by the stamens
that Linnæus sorted out the plants, and although his system is now
obsolete, the stamens are still of prime importance in the classification of genera. But in species, as we have said, all parts of the plant
can be drawn upon for characteristics.

Specific names are generally adjectives ; generic names are in-
variably substantives ; while in the names of the natural orders we
again revert to the adjectival form. Take the *Rosa canina* for
instance: in *canina* we have the adjective agreeing in gender with
the substantive, and out of the substantive we form the adjective
Rosaceæ, the substantive *Plantæ* being understood, the intention
being to describe the order as containing the Rosaceous Plants.

The orders are, in general botany, grouped into Sub-cohorts,
Cohorts, Sub-classes, and Classes ; but with us this elaborate grouping
can be simplified, in words if not in fact, and we can content ourselves with stepping direct from Orders to Classes, and thence to
Divisions.

The Vegetable Kingdom then, is divided into plants that flower,
and plants that do not flower, but reproduce themselves by means of
spores.

Any given plant must consequently be either—

> Phanerogam—Greek, *phaneros*, evident ; from the mode of re-
> production being unconcealed, or,

> Cryptogam—Greek, *cruptos*, hidden ; from the mode of pro-
> duction being concealed.

If our plant be a Cryptogam, it may be either a Cormophyte, that is one provided with stems, leaves and roots, or their morphological equivalents, or it may not. If it is not so provided, it may be either one of the Algæ, the Fungi, or the Protophytes—the three classes of the Thallophyta, as such cryptogamic plants are called as have a mere thallus with no special ascending or descending axis, and no contrast of axis and appendages—but to have included these classes in our book would have made it too large and unwieldy. And for the same reason we have not included the Mosses and Liverworts which form the second class of the Cormophytes, with the first class of which we begin our identifications.

This first class is the Vascularia. To it belong four orders, those of the Ferns, the Lycopods, the Pillworts, and the Horsetails. These are so few that we can dismiss them at once after a very casual glance.

1. Filices—the Ferns—leafy plants of varied structure with the fructification of seeds or sporules which are included in capsules, thecæ or sporangia. These are either naked or covered with a membrane, and are generally collected into clusters on the edge or underside of the leaves.

2. Lycopodiaceæ—the Club Mosses—leafy plants with the fructification in the axils of the leaves or in the bracts of a cone.

3. Marsileaceæ—the Pillworts—plants with slender circinate leaves, with the spores in globular masses, and invested by hardened mucilage.

4. Equisetaceæ—the Horsetails—herbaceous plants with jointed, furrowed, hollow stems, and whorls of scale-like leaves at the joints.

These four orders are so unlike in their British representatives that the distinction between them is easy. And we can profitably devote the rest of our space to the consideration of our flowering plants such as our specimen.

If our plant is not a Cryptogam, it must be a Phanerogam. Now, the Phanerogams are divided into two classes :

1. Dicotyledons (plants with two seed leaves).

2. Monocotyledons (plants with one seed leaf)—all Cryptogamous plants being necessarily Acotyledonous.

This division of plants in accordance with the number of seed leaves is, like all classifications, purely arbitrary. It should never be forgotten that classification is but an aid to memory, and that "natural groups have nuclei but no outlines." Man classifies—not Nature. Man has his "kingdoms," and "divisions," and "classes," and "orders," and "species,"—not Nature. Nature has no pigeon-holes ; her works stand side by side, each growing out of the other, each overlapping the other ; and hard and fast lines and gaps and slips exist only in man's ignorance.

In nearly all systems of classification there are inevitable over-lappings. Even among such a broad group as the Dicotyledons, we shall find a few plants with no cotyledons at all, or with one cotyledon, or with more than two cotyledons ; and so with the other distinctive marks of the class. The statement is disheartening, but it is as well to make it at the outset to avoid misconception. Practically, there is no trouble in sorting out flowering plants into their proper class ; for the sorting is done not on any one character, but on the preponderance of many characters which are held to be more or less distinctive.

It is essential, then, that we give the full definition of our two great classes ; and we cannot do better than quote them from Henfrey.

Class I.—Dicotyledones—Flowering Plants, with stems (when woody) having pith and bark separated by a compact layer of wood, which, in perennial plants, receives annual additions on the outside, beneath the bark ; leaves with the ribs mostly distributed in a netted pattern and generally diminishing in size as they branch ; parts of the floral circles mostly five or four, or some multiple of those numbers, rarely three ; embryo with a pair of cotyledons, and a radicle or primary stem, from the apex of which is developed the primary or tap root.

Class II.—Monocotyledones — Flowering Plants, with stems in which the woody bundles are isolated and diffused through a parenchyma in which there is no distinction of pith and bark, the individual woody bundles rarely being developed further after the fall of the leaves to which they belong ; the leaves (very commonly sheathing at the base) generally with a number of nearly parallel, straight or curved ribs, or with similar ribs given off from a mid-rib ; the cross veins suddenly smaller, occasionally netted-veined ; the flowers generally with three organs in each whorl ; the floral envelopes often all petaloid, or all green or scale-like, rarely with a green calyx and coloured corolla ; seed with an embryo with one cotyledon only.

After due consideration of these carefully-worded definitions of the two great classes, we can resume the identification of our British plant.

If it be a Monocotyledon, it can be assigned either to—

1. Petaloidæ—plants with a perianth ; or,
2. Glumiferæ—plants without a perianth, but with glumes.

If it be one of the Glumiferæ, it must belong either to—

1. Cyperaceæ—the galingale or sedge order—having solid stems often angular, and frequently without joints, and leaves with entire sheaths ; or,
2. Gramineæ—the grass order—having jointed hollow stems and leaves with split sheaths.

There is no need for further detail. If it cannot be assigned to one of these orders, it must be a petaloid.

Of the petaloidæ there are fifteen orders represented in Britain.

Of these five have the ovary inferior, that is below the base of the outer flower circle or perianth, and the rest have it above that base. The five have also the ovary adherent to the perianth tube, while the ten have it free. The five are :—

Orchidaceæ—the orchids.
Iridaceæ—the flags.
Amaryllidaceæ—the daffodils.
Hydrocharidaceæ—the frog bits.
Dioscoreaceæ—the black bryony.

The last we can deal with at once. It is impossible to mistake its one representative. It is a climbing plant. It has netted-veined, bronzed leaves, alternate, broad, heartshaped and stalked. The flowers are small and have bracts, and the stamens and pistils are in separate flowers. The order has but one British genus, and that genus has but one species, the well-known black bryony.

The four are not so easily dismissed. Their leaves are all parallel veined like those of the bulk of the plants among the Monocotyledons, and they all, as we have seen, have the ovary inferior. Let us take the last first.

Hydrocharidaceæ.—Water plants with the leaves floating or sub merged, radical, that is, at the base of the flowering stem, and with serrated margins. Flowers conspicuous and unisexual, and with a spathe. Stamens 3 or 6 free from the style.

We have three left, all with bi-sexual flowers.

Orchidaceæ.—Stamens three, two of which are abortive, so that with one exception (Cypripedium) the British genera have but one perfect anther. Stamens and style united.

Iridaceæ.—Stamens three, none of them abortive. Stamens free from style.

Amaryllidaceæ.—Stamens six, free from style.

These three orders are distinguishable by the stamens alone. There are other differences, of course, but we need not give them here.

We have now to deal with the petaloids having the ovary above the base of the perianth. Of these there are in our country the repre-sentatives of ten orders, of which this is the usual arrangement :—

Liliaceæ—of which the lily is the type.
Trilliaceæ—the herb paris.
Melanthaceæ—the saffron.
Alismaceæ—the water plantain.
Naiadaceæ—the pond weed.
Lemnaceæ—the duckweed.
Araceæ—the lords-and-ladies.
Typhaceæ—the reed-mace (more popularly called the bulrush, a
           name transferred to it from another plant.)
Restiaceæ—the pipe wort.
Juncaceæ—the rush.

Four of these we can sort out at once as having their leaves more or less obscurely net-veined. These are—

Trilliaceæ.	Lemnaceæ.
Alismaceæ.	Araceæ.

The Trilliaceæ are represented by but one genus and one species in our flora. The plant is unmistakable. It is *Paris quadrifolia*. Its flowers are terminal and solitary, and just below them is a whorl of four ovate leaves. The Alismaceæ have a perianth ; the other two orders have none, but one is not likely to be mistaken for the other. The Lemnaceæ are small, stemless, free, floating plants with flowers in the axils of the leaves or at the edge of the frond. The Araceæ are not floating plants : their leaves sheathe at the base, and their flowers are on a spadix enclosed in a leafy sheath. No one would mistake a duckweed for an acorus or an arum. Our ten are thus reduced to—

Liliaceæ.	Typhaceæ.
Melanthaceæ.	Restiaceæ.
Naiadaceæ	Juncaceæ.

The Restiaceæ have but one representative, the water plant *Eriocaulon septangulare.* Though the seven angles may not be very clear, the plant is distinct enough, with its compact scaly head of flowers split up by bracts, and its stem with sheaths slit in the side, without referring to see if the colourless perianth is in two, three, four, five, or six parts, with the two or three stamens adherent to its inner segments.

The Juncaceæ, too, are almost sufficiently familiar. The narrow small round leaves of the rush are known to every child who can identify the order without appealing to the scarious, six-parted perianth, the six or three stamens, and the three stigmas that are sometimes reduced to one.

The points in which the other four differ are as follows :—

Typhaceæ—Perianth wanting ; stamens many.

Naiadaceæ—Perianth of three or four scales or wanting ; stamens four.

Melanthaceæ—Perianth in six. Stamens six. Anthers extrorse, that is, opening outwards. Fruit septicidal.

Liliaceæ—Perianth in six. Stamens six. Anthers introrse, that is, opening inwards. Fruit loculicidal, that is to say, dehiscence takes place through the dorsal sutures so as to open the carpel cavity from behind; whereas, had it been "septicidal," it would have taken place through the septa so as to isolate the previously combined carpels.

We have no more monocotyledonous orders to deal with. Our plant is neither a glumifer nor a petaloid ; it must belong to one of the eighty-one orders that represent the dicotyledons in Britain.

We can treat these conveniently under three divisions :—

1. Polypetalæ, in which both calyx and corolla are generally present, and the corolla consists of distinct petals.
2. Monopetalæ, in which both calyx and corolla are generally present, and the corolla consists of united petals.
3. Incompletæ, in which either the calyx, or the corolla, or both are absent.

Let us take the Incompletæ first. Of these there are two obvious divisions—

1. Plants with both floral envelopes absent;
2. Plants with only one of the floral envelopes absent;

And the first of these can be again obviously divided into

1. Plants with their flowers in catkins;
2. Plants with their flowers not in catkins.

Of these latter there are four orders—

1. Empetraceæ—represented only by the crowberry.
2. Euphorbiaceæ—represented by the spurges, the box, and the mercury.
3. Urticaceæ—represented by the stinging nettle, the pellitory, and the hop.
4. Ulmaceæ—represented by the elm.

The Ulmaceæ are separable at once. To say nothing of their being the only trees of the group, they have the only perfect flowers, that is, the stamens and pistils are found together. Again, the fruit is a samara, that is, it is winged. The stamens are always five. In

Urticaceæ the stamens may be four or five, and the flower is either monœcious, diœcious, or polygamous. In Ulmaceæ the ovary is two celled; in Urticaceæ it is single celled, and the fruit is not a samara.

The Euphorbiaceæ are herbs with milky stems, with the anthers and pistils in different flowers on different plants, and often having the flowers wrapped in an involucre. The Empetraceæ have but one genus in Britain and one species, which is a small shrub with ever-green alternate leaves, bearing diœcious flowers with three stamens. In fact, the stamens alone will distinguish the four orders.

Empetraceæ have three stamens.

Euphorbiaceæ have either one stamen or more than eight.

Urticaceæ have four or five stamens.

Ulmaceæ have four, five, six, seven, or eight, but oftenest five.

From this point of view, the only difficulty is with the last two orders, but the elm tree is never likely to be mistaken for a dusty stinging-nettle, a clinging wall pellitory, or the bold climbing hop.

There are five orders having their flowers in catkins.

Cupuliferæ—the oak, beech, hornbeam, and hazel.

Betulaceæ—the alder and the birch.

Salicaceæ—the poplar and the willow.

Myricaceæ—the bog myrtle.

Coniferæ—the fir, the juniper and the yew.

Of these the Coniferæ are at once distinguishable by their having the male flowers in deciduous catkins, and the female flowers in cones. It is the Conifers which bridge the gap between the flowering plants and the ferns.

The Myricaceæ have but one genus and one species, and this is a small aromatic shrub, with inconspicuous flowers, having from four to eight stamens. The Betulaceæ have from one to four stamens; the Cupuliferæ have from five to twenty stamens; the Salicaceæ have from two to thirty stamens, but have no perianth. To summarise—

Cupuliferæ—fruit in a cup (the acorn, for instance); perianth, five or six-lobed; stamens five to twenty.

Betulaceæ—fruit not in a cup; perianth in four or none; stamens, four; fruit two seeded.

Salicaceæ—fruit not in a cup; perianth, none; stamens, two to thirty; fruit many seeded.

Myricaceæ—fruit a drupe; perianth, none; stamens, four to eight.

We have now to take up the plants that have only one of the floral envelopes absent. Of these there are seven orders, two of which have the ovary inferior, the remainder having it superior. Those with the ovary inferior need not detain us long. They are—

1. Santalaceæ, which have less than six stamens.

2. Aristolochiaceæ, which have six or more stamens.

The others are—

Amaranthaceæ.	Eleagnaceæ.
Chenopodiaceæ.	Thymelaceæ.
Polygonaceæ.	

Amaranthaceæ are represented by one species, which has an unjointed stem, and very tiny flowers in axillary clusters. Eleagnaceæ are also represented by only one species, which has peculiarly

silvery scales and leaves, and no stipules. The male flowers of this
order are in catkins, and it would be placed among the Amentiferæ
were it not for its other characteristics, which ally it closely with the
present group. It is, however, so unmistakable, that it matters very
little where it is placed ; it is the only plant in the flora with silvery
scales and leaves. Thymelaceæ have bi-sexual flowers and eight
stamens, the leaves not being stipuled, and the perianth being
quickly deciduous. The two chief orders of the group are Chenopodiaceæ, with jointed stems and no stipules to the leaves, and
Polygonaceæ, having stems as though with a series of knees, with
large sheathing stipules to the leaves. The state of affairs is thus :—
  1. Amaranthaceæ—no joints, no stipules.
  2. Chenopodiaceæ—joints, no stipules.
  3. Polygonaceæ—joints, large stipules.
  4. Eleagnaceæ—the silvery scales.
  5. Thymelaceæ—the deciduous perianth.
We have now run through the Incompletæ, and the way is clear
for our attack on the great class in which both calyx and corolla are
generally present.
  And first for the Monopetalæ, in which the corolla consists of
inseparate petals.
  These can be divided at the outset into—
  1. Flowers with the ovary inferior.
  2. Flowers with the ovary superior.
  And the latter can be divided into—
  1. Flowers with the stamens on the corolla.
  2. Flowers with the stamens free from corolla.
  The latter has its only representative in the Ericaceæ or Heath tribe.
  The Monopetalous flowers having a superior ovary and stamens on
the corolla can be divided into—
  1. Those having the corolla regular.
  2. Those having the corolla irregular.

  The Monopetalous orders with irregular corollas are :—
  1. Scrophulariaceæ—such as the foxglove.
  2. Orobanchaceæ—such as the broom rape.
  3. Lentibulariaceæ—such as the bladderwort.
  4. Verbenaceæ—such as the vervain.
  5. Labiatæ—such as the dead nettle.
  6. Plantaginaceæ—such as the plantain.
  The Orobanchaceæ are distinguishable at once as being scaly,
leafless root-parasites with brownish flowers, in which are four
stamens, two longer than the rest.
  The Lentibulariaceæ are also unmistakable. They have but two
stamens, and the corolla is two-lipped ; a combination not found in
any other order. They are small marsh herbs, with the leaves radical
and undivided, or else compound and bearing bladders. The
Verbenaceæ have but one representative, the vervain, which is an
erect square-stemmed plant, having opposite three-toothed leaves, a
tubular calyx, a tubular two-lipped corolla, on which are two long and
two short stamens, the flowers being in long spikes.
  Our six orders are thus reduced to three.
      1. Scrophulariaceæ. | 3. Plantaginaceæ.
      2. Labiatæ. |

The last of these are herbaceous plants of humble growth, with undeveloped stems and tufts of ribbed leaves spreading more or less on the ground. There are four stamens which are very long, alternate with the segments of the corolla, and having very lightly attached anthers, and the tubular corolla is very thin, dry and membraneous.

The Labiatæ have square stems and opposite aromatic leaves. The flowers are in whorls or cymes. The calyx is tubular and bilabiate, or in five; the corolla is generally bilabiate. The stamens are two or four, half being longer than the others. The carpels are united into a four-celled ovary, with the style rising between the lobes.

The Scrophulariaceæ contain all the monopetalous flowers with superior ovaries and irregular corollas that do not belong to our five other orders. The main difference between the plants of this order and the Labiates being the absence of the square stem, the two-celled ovary as against the four-lobed one, the terminal style as against the basilar one, and the flowers not being in whorls or cymes.

Our next concern is with the monopetalous plants having a superior ovary, stamens on the corolla, and regular flowers. There are ten orders that can be so grouped. Two of these have the stamens opposite the corolla lobes.

1. Primulaceæ—the primrose tribe.
2. Plumbaginaceæ—the thrift tribe.

The latter of these has a tubular, thin, dry, membraneous calyx, sufficiently distinguishing it from the other orders of the group.

We have thus eight orders left in which the stamens are alternate with the corolla lobes. These we can divide into halves, one half having opposite leaves, and the other alternate leaves. Those with opposite leaves are—

1. Aquifoliaceæ—the holly.
2. Oleaceæ—the privet and the ash.
3. Apocynaceæ—the periwinkle.
4. Gentianaceæ—the gentian.

The holly is the only representative of the Aquifoliaceæ we have. Its spiny leaves and scarlet berries are too well known for us to need to linger over its four or five stamens, and its four or five cleft calyx.

The periwinkles, major and minor, are the only representatives we have of the Apocynaceæ. They have five stamens, and the corolla and calyx are in four or five, generally five, and shaped like a pentagon with bisected sides.

The Oleaceæ are represented by the privet shrub and the ash tree, each having two stamens in their flowers, though the four-cleft corolla and calyx may not exist. These two stamens are a sufficient distinction for our purpose.

The Gentianaceæ are smooth herbs with a bitter juice and strongly-ribbed sessile leaves, having calyx, corolla, and stamens all from four to ten, and a capsular fruit.

The last four orders of our arbitrary grouping have alternate leaves :—

1. Polemoniaceæ—represented by the Jacob's ladder.
2. Convolvulaceæ—the waywind.
3. Solanaceæ—the nightshade.
4. Boraginaceæ—the borage.

The Convolvulaceæ are distinguishable at once by their calyx of five imbricated sepals. The Polemoniaceæ have but one representative, the purplish blue Jacob's ladder, a bold regular flower in fives with a three-celled ovary. The Boraginaceæ are also in fives, but the ovary is four-celled. The Solanaceæ are also in fives, though the stamens number occasionally but four, and the ovary is two-celled. In Solanaceæ the flowers are in axillary cymes; in Boraginaceæ they are in spikes; in Polemonium they are in a panicle. Polemonium, too, has pinnate leaves.

A *spike* is when the flowers are sessile along a single undivided stem. When the flowers are borne on pedicels along such an un-branched rachis, they are said to be in a *raceme*. When the stem is branched and bears two or more flowers, they are said to be in a *panicle*. When several flowers are gathered into a compact cluster, they are said to be *capitate;* when the branches or pedicels appear to start from the same point and are nearly of the same length, the flowers are said to be in an *umbel;* when the lower branches are much longer than the upper, so that although starting from different points, they all attain the same level, and the flowers are in a flat head, the flowers are said to be in a *corymb*. When the flower head is branched, and the flowers open from within outwards in a widening ring, the inflorescence is called a *cyme*. The *inflorescence* of a plant is the arrangement of its flowering branches and the flowers upon them ; its *æstivation* is the arrangement of the sepals or petals in the bud ; its *vernation* is the arrangement of its leaves in the bud.

But we need not overburden ourselves with definitions. We have now the Monopetalous flowers with inferior ovaries. Of these there are seven orders, five of them having the stamens on the corolla, and two having the stamens free of the corolla and on the ovary. These two we will deal with first. They are :—

1. Campanulaceæ—the bell flowers.
2. Vacciniaceæ—the whortleberries.

The first have only five stamens ; the last have eight, nine, or ten stamens, a simple, but for our purposes quite adequate, distinction. We are thus left with the five orders having stamens on the corolla. They are :—

1. Caprifoliaceæ—such as the honeysuckle.
2. Rubiaceæ—such as the madder.
3. Valerianaceæ—such as the valerian.
4. Dipsaceæ—such as the teasel.
5. Compositæ—such as the dandelion.

In this country the Rubiaceæ are represented by herbaceous plants with square stems and whorled leaves, and that distinguishes them at a glance. Of the four orders left, three have four or five stamens ; the fourth, Valerianaceæ, have either one or three stamens, and that sufficiently separates them from the rest.

The Caprifoliaceæ have four or five stamens alternate with the corolla lobes, and the calyx is in four or five, attached to the ovary and having bracts. Their fruit is a berry. They are represented in this country by the elder, the guelder rose, the wayfaring tree, the honeysuckle, and the Linnæa, the characteristics of which will be found fully given in our index of genera.

We are thus left with the Dipsaceæ and the Compositæ. The Dipsaceæ have the calyx in four enclosed in an involucel, the corolla in four, with the limb oblique, four stamens on the corolla, free anthers, and inferior ovary with one pendulous ovule. The Compositæ have the calyx wanting, or with a membraneous or pappose limb, the corolla funnel-shaped, ligulate or bilabiate, nearly always five stamens, connate anthers, and inferior ovary with one erect ovule.

We have now found that our plant belongs neither to the acotyledons, the monocotyledons, the incompletæ nor the monopetalæ. It must therefore belong to the Polypetalæ, the most extensive subdivision of the Dicotyledons. This great subdivision comprising all Dicotyledonous plants with free, separate petals, can be split conveniently enough in two groups.

    1. Those having hypogynous stamens.
    2. Those having perigynous or epigynous stamens.

And the latter can be further divided into—

    1. Those with the ovary superior.
    2. Those with the ovary inferior.

The latter of which can be still further grouped—

    1. Those having four petals or less.
    2. Those having five petals or more.
    3. Those having four or five petals.

The first of these need not detain us long. There are only three orders in the group : one being the Haloragaceæ, in which there are no petals at all, and which consist of aquatic herbs like the marestail, &c., in which the leaves are in whorls ; another, the Loranthaceæ comprising only the parasitic mistletoe in which the leaves are opposite and fleshy, and the fruit a pulpy white berry ; and the other the important willow-herb order, Onagraceæ, in which the calyx is in two or four, tubular, adnate to the ovary and valvate in bud ; the petals are two or four, twisted in æstivation, and the stamens are perigynous and number two, four, or eight.

The orders in the group having always five petals are :—

    1. Cucurbitaceæ, represented in this country by the white bryony, a climbing herb, with alternate palmate leaves, tendrils, greenish flowers, parts in five, and red berries.
    2. Araliaceæ, represented amongst us by the climbing ivy, and the green cubical flowered moschatel.
    3. Umbelliferæ, the great order whose umbelled flowers and simple or deeply divided sheathing leaves are so unmistakable, however embarrassing may be its detail in genera and species.

There are two orders, having sometimes four, and sometimes five petals. These are Grossulariaceæ and Cornaceæ. In Grossulariaceæ the leaves are rough, lobed and alternate ; in the other order they are simple, ovate and opposite. Grossulariaceæ are represented with us by the one genus Ribes, of which the black and red currants are the most appreciated species. Cornaceæ also have but one genus, Cornus, the dogwood common in our hedges, and the detailed description of which we can very well reserve till we deal with genera and species. In no way are they likely to be mistaken for the marestail, the mistletoe, the willow herb, the white bryony, or the ivy, and any doubt that may arise between the Cornacæ and Umbelliferæ will be set at rest at once by a look at the leaves

The polypetalous orders with stamens arranged round or on a superior ovary are—

1. Celastraceæ—such as the spindle tree.
2. Rhamnaceæ—such as the buckthorn.
3. Leguminosæ—such as the furze.
4. Rosaceæ—such as the rose.
5. Lythraceæ—such as the purple loose-strife.
6. Tamariscaceæ—such as the tamarisk.
7. Portulaceæ—such as the blinks.
8. Illecebraceæ—such as the strapwort.
9. Scleranthaceæ—such as the knawel.
10. Crassulaceæ—such as the stone-crop.
11. Saxifragaceæ—such as the London pride.

The Leguminosæ are distinguishable at once by their papilionaceous corollas. The Rosaceæ need no lengthened notice; their characteristics are so well marked—alternate leaves with a stipule on each side of the petiole base, calyx four or five lobed, free or adherent to ovary, petals five, equal, stamens many and curved inwards in æstivation, and fruit never a legume. Obvious enough, too, are the tamarisks. There is but one of them in this country, a straggling coniferous-looking shrub with twiggy branches and scale-like leaves, and flowers small and regular in lateral spikes, and having all their parts in four or five. Portulaceæ, too, with their single representative, the miserable little blinks, can hardly stop the way, as fortunately the two sepals only mark them off from the rest; and Illecebraceæ with their sessile leaves, and Scleranthaceæ with their connate leaves, are also sufficiently recognisable.

We are thus left with—

Celastraceæ—stamens four or five, alternate with petals.

Rhamnaceæ—stamens four or five, opposite petals.

Lythraceæ—stamens three or six or twelve, leaves opposite or whorled.

Crassulaceæ—stamens three to twenty; thick, fleshy leaves; flowers symmetrical.

Saxifragaceæ—stamens five or ten; styles two, diverging; flowers unsymmetrical.

And now our road is clear for noting the distinctions by which the orders can most easily be sorted out among such of the polypetalous plants as have their stamens rising from beneath the ovary.

It will simplify matters to consider five of these orders by themselves.

1. Caryophyllaceæ—a well marked order, mostly with stems tumid at the joints; leaves at the joints entire and opposite, flowers regular, sepals four or five, distinct or connected in a tube, petals four or five, clawed, stamens four, five, eight or ten; anthers opening longitudinally, capsule opening at the top with teeth. The commonest plants of the order are the stitch-worts, pinks, and campions.

2. Aceraceæ—an order with only one genus, and that of only two species, one of which is the maple tree, and the other the sycamore tree, sufficient descriptions of which will be found in the index. The stamens number from five to twelve,

3. Droseraceæ—an order with but one genus, having the three sundews as its representatives. Its stamens are either five or ten—but further description can be postponed for our index.

4. Elatinaceæ—an order with only one genus, which is represented by the two waterworts, and for which see the index to the genera. Its stamens may be either three, five, six or ten.

5. Ranunculaceæ for the one genus *Myosurus*, for which see the index to genera.

These caryophylls, and acers, the little insectivorous sundew, the tiny water herb, and the eccentric mousetail, are so unlike each other, and so unlike all the other orders we have left to us, that their sorting out in this way will embarrass no one.

We have, then, eighteen orders left. We can group them most easily into those having ten or more stamens and those having less than ten stamens, the four orders we have just parted with being those in which the number of the stamens would overlap and render such grouping impossible.

Polypetalous plants, with stamens hypogynous and less than ten:—

1. Berberidaceæ—three, four, or six stamens; a spiny shrub, the spines being in threes.

2. Fumariaceæ—six stamens in two bundles; slender herbs, with brittle stems.

3. Cruciferæ—six stamens, two shorter than the rest; herbs with alternate leaves.

4. Violaceæ—five stamens, the connective produced above the anther cells.

5. Polygalaceæ—eight stamens in two bundles; small herbs, with irregular flowers.

6. Frankeniaceæ—four, five, or six stamens; a low branched herb with opposite leaves and red flowers.

7. Linaceæ—four or five stamens, alternate with petals, with small teeth between them; flowers blue or white.

8. Balsaminaceæ—five stamens; a succulent herb, with axillary yellow flowers.

Here at a glance we have just enough to enable us to place a plant in its proper order, and the other detail we can reserve for our alphabetical list.

Our next group will be Polypetalous plants, with stamens hypogynous and ten or more.

1. Ranunculaceæ—stamens, twelve or more.

2. Nymphæaceæ—stamens many, partially petaloid.

3. Papaveraceæ—stamens many.

4. Resedaceæ—stamens, ten or more.

5. Cistaceæ—stamens many.

6. Malvaceæ—stamens many, united into a tube.

7. Tiliaceæ—stamens many.

8. Hypericaceæ—stamens many, united into three to five bundles.

9. Geraniaceæ—stamens ten.

10. Oxalidaceæ—stamens ten, five longer than the others.

Here Nymphæaceæ, the water lily order, Malvaceæ, the mallow order, Hypericaceæ, the St. John's wort order, and Oxalidaceæ, the wood sorrel order, are at once distinguishable from the rest and from each other. The Resedaceæ, the mignonette order, is represented by only one genus, Reseda, which is not likely to be assigned to the Geraniaceæ, as it has neither the habit, the swollen stem, the clawed petals, nor the beaked fruit, as noted in our index to the genera.

Our many-stamened orders are thus reduced to—

1. Ranunculaceæ.	3. Cistaceæ.
2. Papaveraceæ.	4. Tiliaceæ.

Now Tiliaceæ has but one genus amongst us, and that is Tilia, to which belong the three species of lime tree. Its leaves are lop-sided, alternate and stipulate; its flowers are regular and greenish; its sepals are four or five, and deciduous; its petals are four or five; and, generally speaking, it would be like the Malvaceæ, if the stamens were united as in that order.

Cistaceæ has but one genus amongst us, and that is Helianthemum the rock rose, which is a shrubby herb, never over a foot high, and bearing a white or yellow flower, having five sepals, two smaller than the rest and three twisted in the bud, and five petals crumpled and twisted in the bud the contrary way to the sepals. The rock rose, in fact, is not likely to be mistaken for a lime tree.

Papaveraceæ is the poppy order. It consists of herbs with white or coloured milky juice, leaves alternate, simple, or lobed, and without stipules; flowers regular, fugacious, and usually crumpled in æstivation and nodding in bud; sepals two, or very occasionally three, disappearing early; petals four, rarely five or six; and a capsular fruit.

We have but one order left, the Ranunculaceæ. It comprises land and water herbs and a climbing shrub, all having colourless, acrid juice. Its leaves are generally deeply divided and nearly always alternate, and occasionally they have dilated sheathing petioles. Its flowers are regular or irregular, and of all colours. Its sepals are three, five or six, green or petaloid; its petals are five or more, free and often irregular; its stamens are (with the exception of *Myosurus*) twelve or more, and hypogynous, as we have seen; and its anthers are adnate and mostly reversed.

To the Ranunculaceæ our plant belongs. But before we proceed further with its identification it is desirable that we should give in tabular form the classification we have adopted, and which, let it be clearly understood, is only entirely applicable to our country's flowers.

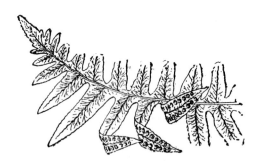

CHAPTER III.

TABULAR SCHEME.

PHANEROGAMS, or Flowering Plants.
Cryptogams, or Flowerless Plants.

CRYPTOGAMS—

Equisetaceæ—jointed stems ; scale-like leaves in a whorl.

Marsileaceæ—spores in globular mass at leaf base.

Lycopodiaceæ—fructification axillary or in cone bracts.

Filices.

PHANEROGAMS—

1. Monocotyledones.

2. Dicotyledones.

MONOCOTYLEDONES—

1. Petaloidæ.

2. Glumiferæ.

GLUMIFERÆ.

Cyperaceæ—solid stem ; sheaths entire.
Gramineæ—hollow stem ; sheaths split.

PETALOIDÆ.

1. Ovary superior.
2. Ovary inferior.
   Ovary inferior—
       Orchidaceæ—stamens three, one or two abortive.
       Iridaceæ—stamens three, all perfect.
       Amaryllidaceæ—stamens six.
       Hydrocharidaceæ—water plants, leaves radical.
       Dioscoreaceæ—climber ; alternate, cordate leaves.
   Ovary superior—
       1. Leaves netted veined.
       2. Leaves parallel veined.
          Leaves netted veined—
              Trilliaceæ—leaves in fours.
              Alismaceæ—perianth six ; stamens six.
              Lemnaceæ—floating plants ; no perianth.
              Araceæ—no perianth ; flowers on spadix in sheath.
          Leaves parallel veined—
              Liliaceæ—stamens six ; anthers introrse.
              Melanthaceæ—stamens six ; anthers extrorse.
              Naiadaceæ—stamens four.
              Typhaceæ—no perianth.
              Restiaceæ—stamens two or three.
              Juncaceæ—round leaves.

DICOTYLEDONES—
  1. Incompletæ.
  2. Monopetalæ.
  3. Polypetalæ.
INCOMPLETÆ.
  1. Both envelopes absent.
  2. Only one envelope absent.
    Both envelopes absent.
      1. Flowers not in catkins.
      2. Flowers in catkins.
      Flowers not in catkins—
        Empetraceæ—stamens three.
        Euphorbiaceæ—stamens one, or more than eight.
        Urticaceæ—stamens four or five.
        Ulmaceæ—trees ; flowers perfect.
      Flowers in catkins—
        Cupuliferæ—stamens five or more ; fruit in a cup.
        Betulaceæ—stamens four ; fruit two-seeded.
        Salicaceæ—stamens two to thirty ; fruit many seeded.
        Myricaceæ—stamens two to eight ; fruit a drupe.
        Coniferæ.
    One floral envelope absent.
      1. Ovary inferior.
      2. Ovary superior.
      Ovary inferior—
        Santalaceæ—stamens less than six.
        Aristolochiaceæ—stamens six or more.
      Ovary superior—
        Amaranthaceæ—stem not jointed ; stamens three to five.
        Chenopodiaceæ—stem jointed, no stipules.
        Polygonaceæ—stem jointed, sheathing stipules.
        Eleagnaceæ—silvery scales.
        Thymelaceæ—stem not jointed ; stamens eight.
MONOPETALÆ.
  1. Ovary superior.
  2. Ovary inferior.
    Ovary superior—
      1. Stamens free from corolla.
      2. Stamens on corolla.
      Stamens free from corolla—
        Ericaceæ.
      Stamens on corolla.
        1. Corolla irregular.
        2. Corolla regular.
        Corolla irregular—
          Orobanchaceæ—leafless root parasites.
          Lentibulariaceæ—marsh plants ; two stamens.
          Plantaginaceæ—stamens four, very long.
          Verbenaceæ—leaves with three teeth.
          Labiatæ—square stem ; basilar style.
          Scrophulariaceæ.

MONOPETALÆ—(*continued*).
    Corolla regular—
        1. Stamens opposite corolla lobes.
        2. Stamens alternate with corolla lobes.
        Stamens opposite corolla lobes—
            Plumbaginaceæ—membraneous calyx.
            Primulaceæ.
        Stamens alternate with corolla lobes.
           1. Opposite leaves.
           2. Alternate leaves.
           Opposite leaves—
              Aquifoliaceæ—spiny leaves; axillary flowers.
              Oleaceæ—stamens two.
              Apocynaceæ—pentagonal corolla.
              Gentianaceæ.
           Alternate leaves—
              Polemoniaceæ—flowers in panicle.
              Convolvulaceæ—five imbricated sepals.
              Solanaceæ—flowers in axillary cymes.
              Boraginaceæ.
    Ovary inferior—
        1. Stamens free of corolla.
        2. Stamens on corolla.
        Stamens free of corolla—
            Campanulaceæ—five stamens.
            Vacciniaceæ—eight, nine, or ten stamens.
        Stamens on corolla—
            Caprifoliaceæ—fruit a berry.
            Rubiaceæ—square stems, whorled leaves.
            Valerianaceæ—one or three stamens.
            Dipsaceæ—involucel.
            Compositæ.

POLYPETALÆ.
    1. Stamens not hypogynous.
    2. Stamens hypogynous.
    Stamens not hypogynous.
        1. Ovary inferior.
        2. Ovary superior.
        Ovary inferior—
           1. With four petals or less.
           2. With five petals or more.
           3. With four or five petals.
         With four petals or less—
            Haloragaceæ—no petals.
            Loranthaceæ—fleshy leaves.
            Onagraceæ.
         With five petals or more—
            Cucurbitaceæ—climber, with tendrils.
            Umbelliferæ—leaves simple, or compound and alternate.
            Araliaceæ—leaves smooth, lobed, and alternate.
        With four or five petals—
            Grossulariaceæ—leaves rough, lobed, and alternate.
            Cornaceæ—leaves smooth, ovate, and opposite.

POLYPETALÆ—(*continued*).

Ovary superior—

Celastraceæ—stamens four or five, alternate with petals.

Rhamnaceæ—stamens four or five, opposite petals.

Leguminosæ—papilionaceous corolla.

Lythraceæ—stamens three, six, or twelve ; style filiform.

Tamariscaceæ—scale-like leaves.

Portulaceæ—two sepals.

Illecebraceæ—sessile leaves.

Scleranthaceæ—connate leaves.

Crassulaceæ—thick fleshy leaves ; flowers symmetrical.

Saxifragaceæ—styles two, diverging ; flowers unsymmetrical.

Rosaceæ.

Stamens hypogynous.

　1. Stamens over or under ten.

　2. Stamens less than ten.

　3. Stamens ten or more.

Stamens over or under ten—

Caryophyllaceæ—jointed stems, opposite leaves.

Aceraceæ—trees ; fruit a samara.

Droseraceæ—marsh herbs ; glandular leaves.

Elatinaceæ—water herbs ; spathulate leaves.

Ranunculaceæ—in respect of the one genus *Myosurus*, which usually has but five stamens.

Stamens less than ten—

Berberidaceæ—three, four, or six stamens ; spines in threes.

Fumariaceæ—six stamens, in two bundles.

Cruciferæ—stamens four long, two short.

Violaceæ—five stamens, connective above the anther cells.

Polygalaceæ—eight stamens in two bundles.

Frankeniaceæ—four, five, or six stamens ; flowers red.

Linaceæ—four or five stamens ; flowers blue or white.

Balsaminaceæ—five stamens ; flowers yellow.

Stamens ten or more—

Nymphæaceæ—water plants ; stamens petaloid.

Malvaceæ—stamens united into tube.

Hypericaceæ—stamens in three, four or five bundles.

Oxalidaceæ—stamens five long, and five short.

Resedaceæ—stamens on glandular irregular disk, petals lacerated.

Geraniaceæ—stamens ten ; long-beaked fruit.

Tiliaceæ—trees ; leaves with stipules.

Cistaceæ—sepals five, three twisted in bud, two small or wanting.

Papaveraceæ — sepals two or three, caducous ; flowers crumpled in bud.

Ranunculaceæ.

CHAPTER IV.

THE NATURAL ORDERS,

THE preceding classification being designed solely as a ready means of identifying the flowers, takes but little note of the relationship of the different orders. For purposes of comparison and reference, it is necessary that the usual arrangement should be given; and the examples on our coloured plates are grouped accordingly :—

    1. Phanerogamia (flowering plants).
    2. Cryptogamia (flowerless plants).

PHANEROGAMIA—
    1. Dicotyledones (Exogens).
    2. Monocotyledones (Endogens).
        Dicotyledones—
            1. Polypetalæ.

523

            2. Monopetalæ.
            3. Incompletæ.

POLYPETALÆ—
Stamens hypogynous.
Stamens perigynous or epigynous.

STAMENS HYPOGYNOUS—
Ranunculaceæ.—Sepals three, five, or six, green or petaloid; petals five or more, free, and often irregular; stamens 12 or more, except in *Myosurus*, which has but five; anthers adnate, and mostly reversed; fruit of distinct carpels or single-seeded achenes. Herbs, and a climbing shrub, with colourless acrid juice; leaves generally divided and alternate, and often with dilated sheathing petioles.

Berberidaceæ.—Sepals three, four, or six in a double row, bracteated and deciduous; petals three, four, or six, free, glandular at the base; stamens three, four, or six; fruit, a berry. Spiny shrubs, the spines being in threes; leaves alternate, compound, exstipulate, and ciliated on the serratures; flowers pendulous.

Nymphæaceæ.—Sepals four, five, or six, partially petaloid, passing into numerous petals and stamens, imbricated in several rows, and placed on a fleshy disk surrounding a many-celled, many-seeded ovary. Aquatic herbs; with cordate or peltate floating leaves, and showy, solitary flowers.

Papaveraceæ.—Sepals two, occasionally three, deciduous; petals four, rarely five or six; stamens many and free; fruit capsular or pod-shaped, with parietal placentas. Herbs; with white or coloured milky juice; leaves alternate, simple or lobed, and exstipulate; flowers regular, fugacious, and usually crumpled and nodding in bud.

D 2

STAMENS HYPOGYNOUS—(*continued*).

Fumariaceæ.—Sepals two, deciduous; petals four, parallel, one or two swollen at the base; stamens six, in two bundles, opposite to the outer petals; ovary single-celled with two opposite parietal placentas. Slender herbs; with brittle stems and watery juice; leaves alternate, divided, and exstipulate; flowers irregular and in racemes.

Cruciferæ.—Sepals four, deciduous; petals four, stalked, cruciform; stamens six, four longer than the rest; fruit, a pouch or pod. Herbs with not unwholesome pungent watery juice; leaves alternate and without stipules; flowers regular, beginning in corymbs and becoming racemose.

Resedaceæ.—Sepals four, five or six, persistent; petals four, five or six, irregular, lacerated; stamens ten or more, on a glandular, irregular disk; ovary three-lobed, single-celled. Leaves alternate, without stipules; flowers oblique and greenish.

Cistaceæ.—Sepals five, two smaller than the rest and three twisted in the bud; petals five, crumpled and twisted in the bud the contrary way to the sepals; stamens many and free; ovary tripartite and single-celled. Herbaceous plants or shrubs; with entire leaves and regular flowers.

Violaceæ.—Sepals five, persistent and imbricate; petals five, unequal, with the lower one spurred at the base; stamens five, with the connective produced above the anther cells; ovary tripartite and single-celled. Leaves alternate and with stipules; flowers irregular and axillary.

Droseraceæ.—Sepals five, imbricate and persistent; petals five; stamens five or ten, free; ovary single-celled. Marsh herbs; radical leaves with glandular capitate hairs; flowers regular.

Polygalaceæ.—Sepals five, the two inner petaloid; petals three, four, or five, one longer than the rest; stamens eight, in two bundles; capsule two-celled. Herbs; with simple alternate leaves without stipules; flowers irregular.

Frankeniaceæ.—Sepals four, five, or six, combined into a furrowed tube; petals four, five, or six, clawed; stamens four, five, or six, free, alternating with petals; ovary single-celled, with two or four valves. Low, branched herb; leaves opposite, without stipules, but with a membraneous sheathing base. Flowers red, small, axillary.

Elatinaceæ.—Sepals three to five; petals three to five, sessile stamens three to five, or six to ten, free; capsule three to five-valved. Small marsh herbs; leaves in a whorl, spathulate, and with stipules.

Caryophyllaceæ.—Sepals four or five, distinct or connected in a tube; petals four or five, clawed; stamens as many as or double the number of petals; anthers opening longitudinally; capsule opening at the top with teeth. Herbs; generally with stems tumid at the joints; leaves entire and opposite; flowers regular.

Linaceæ.—Sepals four or five, persistent, imbricate in bud; petals four or five, fugacious, twisted in bud, and clawed; stamens four or five, alternate with petals, with small teeth between them; capsule three, four, or five-celled. Herbs; with entire leaves, having no stipules.

STAMENS HYPOGYNOUS—(*continued*).

Malvaceæ.—Sepals five, valvate in bud; petals five, twisted in bud; stamens many, twisted into a tube adherent to the claws of the petals; ovary, many-celled. Herbs, shrubs or trees; leaves alternate with stipules, and generally covered with soft down; flowers regular and axillary.

Tiliaceæ.—Sepals four or five, valvate in bud, deciduous; petals four or five, often with a depression at the base; stamens many, not united as in Malvaceæ. Leaves unequal sided, alternate, and with stipules; flowers regular and inconspicuous, springing from a lanceolate leafy bract.

Hypericaceæ.—Sepals four or five, persistent, imbricate, and often dotted; petals four or five, twisted in bud and often dotted; stamens many and united into three or five bundles; capsule three, four, or five-celled. Herbs or shrubs; leaves generally opposite, without stipules and marked with pellucid dots; flowers yellow.

Aceraceæ.—Sepals four to nine; petals four to nine, imbricate in bud; stamens five to twelve on a disk; carpels two; fruit, a samara. Trees; leaves simple, generally lobed, opposite and without stipules; flowers green and small.

Geraniaceæ.—Sepals five, imbricate in bud; petals five, clawed, and twisted in bud; stamens ten; carpels five, elastic, combined into a pistil with five cells and a long beak. Herbs; with swollen stem joints; leaves lobed and stipuled, opposite, or alternate and then opposite the peduncles.

Balsaminaceæ.—Sepals five, irregular, deciduous, imbricate in bud, one of them spurred; petals four, irregular, united in pairs: stamens five, filaments more or less united at the end; capsule bursting elastically. Succulent herbs; leaves without stipules, simple and alternate; flowers axillary and yellow.

Oxalidaceæ.—Sepals five, imbricate in bud; petals five, often coherent at the base, twisted in bud; stamens ten, five opposite the petals and longer than the rest; carpels united into a pistil with five polyspermous cells; fruit bursting elastically. Small herbs; leaves mostly trifoliate, acid, and sensitive; flowers axillary.

STAMENS PERIGYNOUS OR EPIGYNOUS.

Celastraceæ.—Calyx four or five cleft, imbricate in bud; petals four or five, inserted into the margin of a hypogynous fleshy disk: stamens four or five, alternate with the petals; seed with bright orange-coloured arillus. Shrubs or trees; leaves simple and mostly opposite; flowers in axillary cymes.

Rhamnaceæ.—Calyx four or five cleft, valvate in bud; petals four or five on the top of the calyx tube, and alternate with its lobes; stamens four or five, opposite the petals; ovary superior, three-celled, seeds solitary and erect. Shrubs with simple and usually alternate leaves; flowers small and greenish.

Leguminosæ.—Calyx four or five cleft; petals five, irregular, springing from the bottom of the calyx; stamens ten; carpel solitary, superior, ripening into a legume. Herbs or shrubs; mostly with ternate or pinnate leaves, alternate and stipuled, with or without tendrils; flowers papilionaceous.

STAMENS PERIGYNOUS OR EPIGYNOUS—(*continued*).

Rosaceæ.—Calyx four or five-lobed, free, or adherent with ovary ; petals five, equal ; stamens varying in number, generally being more than twelve, and curving inwards in bud ; ovary superior and double-celled ; fruit various, but never a legume. Shrubs or herbs ; leaves alternate with a stipule on each side of the base of the petiole.

Onagraceæ.—Calyx in two or four, tubular, adnate with the ovary and valvate in bud ; petals two or four, twisted in bud ; stamens two, four, or eight ; ovary inferior, one to four-celled, many seeded ; fruit, a berry or capsule. Herbs or shrubs ; leaves entire; frequently opposite and never dotted ; flowers regular and showy.

Haloragaceæ.—Calyx in three or four, adnate with ovary ; petals generally wanting ; stamens one, two, four, or eight ; ovary inferior and one to four-celled ; seeds solitary, pendulous, and perispermic. Aquatic herbs ; leaves often whorled ; flowers very small.

Lythraceæ.—Calyx in three, often with intermediate teeth ; petals three or six, crumpled in bud ; stamens six or twelve ; ovary superior. Herbs ; generally with opposite entire leaves and without stipules ; flowers regular.

Tamariscaceæ.—Calyx in four or five ; petals four or five, rising from the base of the calyx ; stamens four, five, eight or ten ; ovary superior. Shrubs ; with twiggy branches and scale-like leaves ; flowers in lateral spikes, small and regular.

Cucurbitaceæ.—Calyx five-cleft, the tube adnate with the ovary ; petals five, often with netted veins ; stamens five, more or less cohering ; ovary inferior ; fruit fleshy ; seeds flat in an arillus. Succulent climbing plants ; leaves with tendrils in the place of stipules ; flowers in axillary racemes.

Portulaceæ.—Sepals two, rarely three or five, coherent at base, imbricate in bud ; petals five, inserted into the base of the calyx; stamens of uncertain number, generally three or five ; ovary superior and single-celled. Succulent herbs; with opposite leaves.

Illecebraceæ.—Sepals four or five ; petals four or five, or wanting ; stamens five or less ; ovary superior. Branching herbs ; leaves entire and sessile ; flowers small.

Scleranthaceæ.—Calyx in four or five ; petals wanting ; stamens ten or less ; ovary superior. Tufted herbs ; with opposite, connate leaves and axillary flowers.

Grossulariaceæ.—Calyx four or five-cleft growing from top of ovary; petals four or five, at the mouth of the calyx throat ; stamens four or five, alternate with petals ; ovary inferior ; fruit, a pulpy berry. Shrubs; often spiny ; leaves rough, lobed and alternate ; flowers small and greenish.

Crassulaceæ.—Sepals three to twenty, united at the base ; petals three to twenty, inserted at the base of the sepals ; stamens three to twenty, or twice as many as petals; carpels three to twenty, superior, opposite the petals, and many-seeded. Succulent herbs ; leaves thick, fleshy and without stipules ; flowers symmetrical.

Stamens Perigynous or Epigynous—(*continued*).

Saxifragaceæ.—Petals four or five, or wanting ; stamens five or ten, distinct ; ovary superior ; carpels united into a pistil, with two many-seeded cells, and two diverging styles. Small herbs ; mostly mountainous ; flowers regular but not symmetrical.

Araliaceæ.—Calyx three or five-cleft, half inferior ; petals five or ten, occasionally wanting ; stamens as many or twice as many as the petals from the margin of an epigynous disk ; ovary inferior, with two or more cells having a style to each ; fruit fleshy and dry, of several single-seeded cells. Climbing shrubs or low herbs ; with alternate lobed leaves and green flowers.

Cornaceæ.—Calyx in four or five attached to the ovary ; petals four or five, broad at the base ; stamens four or five, inserted with the petals ; ovary inferior ; style filiform ; stigma simple; fruit, a drupe, with a two-celled nut. Herbs or trees ; with opposite ovate leaves; flowers small, in heads or umbels.

Umbelliferæ.—Calyx in five, teeth minute or often wanting ; petals five, often unequal ; stamens five, epigynous, alternate with the petals and springing with them from a thick fleshy disk at the base of the two styles ; seeds one in each of the two carpels, adherent, pendulous and albuminous. Herbs ; generally with fistular stems, leaves alternate, without stipules, deeply divided and sheathing at the base ; flowers in umbels and mostly white.

Loranthaceæ.—Calyx adnate with the inferior ovary ; petals four. stamens four, epiphyllous, stamens and pistils often in different plants ; fruit, a pulpy berry. Parasitic shrubs ; with entire opposite fleshy leaves without stipules.

Monopetalæ—
Ovary inferior.
Ovary superior.
Ovary Inferior—

Caprifoliaceæ.—Calyx in four or five, attached to the ovary and having bracts ; corolla four or five-cleft ; stamens four or five on the corolla, and alternate with its lobes ; ovary three, four, or five-celled ; fruit, not a drupe. Shrubs or herbs ; with opposite leaves, generally without stipules.

Rubiaceæ.—Calyx and corolla each in four or five ; stamens four or five on the corolla, and alternate with its lobes ; ovary two-celled, with solitary erect ovules and two styles. Herbaceous plants (in this country) with square stems and whorled leaves.

Valerianaceæ.—Calyx in five, with one limb becoming membranous or pappose ; corolla five ; stamens three, on the corolla ; carpels solitary, with one pendulous ovule. Herbs ; generally aromatic, with opposite leaves and without stipules.

Dipsaceæ.—Calyx in four, enclosed in an involucel ; corolla in four with the limb oblique ; stamens four on the corolla ; anthers free ; carpel solitary, with one pendulous ovule. Herbs ; leaves opposite or whorled ; flowers in heads.

Compositæ.—Calyx wanting, or with a membranous or pappose limb ; corolla funnel-shaped, ligulate, or bilabiate, or wanting ; stamens five on the corolla ; anthers united into a tube round the style ; ovary with one erect ovule. Herbs or shrubs ; flowers in a dense head on a common receptacle surrounded by an involucre.

OVARY INFERIOR—*(continued)*.

Campanulaceæ.—Calyx in five, lobes persistent ; corolla in five ; stamens five, on the ovary ; filaments broad and valvate at base ; ovary two to eight-celled ; style thick and hairy. Herbs ; with entire alternate leaves without stipules.

Vacciniaceæ.—Calyx in four or five ; corolla in four or five ; stamens eight or ten, on the four or five-celled ovary ; fruit a berry. Shrubs with alternate leaves ; flowers solitary and regular.

OVARY SUPERIOR—

Ericaceæ.—Calyx in four or five ; corolla in four or five ; stamens eight or ten, free from corolla ; ovary on a disk with four or more cells. Shrubs ; leaves mostly rigid, evergreen, and without stipules.

Aquifoliaceæ.—Calyx in four or six, lobes imbricated ; corolla four or six imbricated in bud ; stamens four or six, on the corolla, and alternate with the lobes ; fruit a fleshy berry. Evergreen trees or shrubs ; leaves simple, prickly, and without stipules ; flowers axillary.

Oleaceæ.—Calyx in four, sometimes wanting ; corolla in four, valvate in bud, sometimes wanting ; stamens two, on the corolla ; ovary without hypogynous disk ; fruit a berry or key. Trees or shrubs ; leaves simple or compound, opposite and without stipules.

Apocynaceæ—Calyx in five ; corolla in five, twisted in the bud ; stamens five, on the corolla ; stigma shaped like an hour glass ; fruit of two follicles. Shrubs ; often with milky juice ; leaves entire, opposite and without stipules ; flowers purple and pentagonal.

Gentianaceæ.—Calyx four to ten-lobed ; corolla four to ten-lobed ; stamens on the corolla and alternate with its lobes ; ovary single or double celled ; fruit a capsule or berry. Smooth herbs ; leaves entire, sessile, ribbed, generally opposite and without stipules.

Polemoniaceæ.—Calyx in five ; corolla in five ; stamens five on the corolla ; fruit a three-celled capsule, three-valved, with the valves separating from the axis. Herbs ; leaves generally pinnate and alternate.

Convolvulaceæ.—Calyx of five sepals imbricated in two rows. corolla in four or five with limb plaited ; stamens four or five, on the corolla ; carpels united into a two or three-celled few-seeded pistil, with erect ovules. Herbs ; generally twining ; leaves or scales alternate.

Solanaceæ.—Calyx in four or five ; corolla in five ; stamens five, on the corolla and alternate with its segments ; carpels united into a two-celled many-seeded pistil. Herbs ; with colourless juice ; leaves alternate, and without stipules ; flowers often extra axillary.

Scrophulariaceæ.—Calyx in four or five ; corolla in four or five, imbricated in bud, and irregular ; stamens two or four, rarely equal, generally two longer than the others ; fruit a capsule. Leaves generally opposite, but irregular ; flowers irregular.

Orobanchaceæ.—Calyx in four or five ; corolla in four or five, gaping ; stamens four, two long and two short ; ovary single-celled. Leafless root parasites with brownish flowers,

OVARY SUPERIOR—(*continued*).

Verbenaceæ.—Calyx tubular ; corolla tubular and trifid ; stamens on the corolla, two long and two short ; ovary four-celled ; fruit a capsule of four nutlets. Stem square ; leaves opposite, and three-toothed.

Labiatæ.—Calyx tubular, bilabiate or in five ; corolla monopetalous, hypogynous and generally bilabiate ; stamens two or four, on the corolla, half longer than the rest ; carpels united into a four-celled ovary, with the style rising between the lobes. Herbs with square stems ; leaves generally opposite and aromatic ; flowers irregular and in whorls or cymes.

Boraginaceæ.—Calyx in five ; corolla in five, regular, imbricated in bud ; stamens five on the corolla, and alternate with its segments ; carpels united into a four-lobed ovary ; fruit of four nutlets. Herbs; with rough alternate leaves, and flowers in spikes.

Lentibulariaceæ.—Calyx in four or five ; corolla in four or five, or two-lipped with a spur ; stamens two, on the corolla ; ovary single-celled; fruit a many-seeded capsule. Small marsh herbs ; leaves radical and undivided, or compound and bearing bladders.

Primulaceæ—Calyx in four to seven ; corolla in four to seven ; stamens four to seven, on the corolla, and opposite its segments ; ovary unilocular, with a free central placenta bearing numerous ovules, each with two coats ; fruit a many-seeded capsule. Leaves simple, opposite, or alternate ; flowers regular.

Plumbaginaceæ.—Calyx tubular, in five, membranous; corolla in five, regular; stamens, five, on the corolla; styles five; stigmas five; ovary single-celled, single-seeded. Shrubby herbs; leaves radical or alternate.

Plantaginaceæ.—Calyx in four; corolla, very thin, in four; stamens, four, on corolla, and elongated; carpel solitary, with a single stigma. Herbs ; with undeveloped stems, leaves radical, spreading, and entire, and spikes of small greenish flowers.

INCOMPLETÆ—

Plants wanting corolla.

Plants wanting both corolla and calyx.

PLANTS WANTING COROLLA—

Amaranthaceæ.—Perianth in three or five, often with bracts; flowers unisexual; stamens three to five, hypogynous, and opposite the perianth segments; anthers often unilocular; ovary superior; single or double celled; styles one, or wanting; fruit indehiscent. Weedy herbs; stems not jointed; leaves without stipules.

Chenopodiaceæ.—Perianth in five, imbricate in bud, free, deeply cleft, generally without bracts; flowers often unisexual; stamens one, two or five, generally five, rising from the base of the perianth and opposite the segments; anthers two-celled; ovary superior; style divided and rarely simple; fruit indehiscent, enclosed in the perianth, which often becomes fleshy. Weedy herbs with jointed stems; leaves generally small and without stipules

PLANTS WANTING COROLLA—(*continued*).

Polygonaceæ.—Perianth in five, free, divided, the segments often in a double row; flowers mostly bisexual; stamens five to eight; ovary superior, with two or more styles or sessile stigmas; fruit, a flattened or triangular nut usually enclosed in the sepals. Herbs with swollen joints in the stem; leaves alternate, with sheathing stipules.

Eleagnaceæ.—Male flowers in catkins; perianth in three or four; stamens four to eight, inserted on the throat; ovary superior; fruit crustaceous. Shrubs; with silvery scales entire leaves, alternate and without stipules.

Thymelaceæ.—Perianth free, tubular, and in four or five; stamens eight, inserted upon the tube; anthers two-celled, opening longitudinally; ovary superior and single-celled, with one pendulous ovule; style one; stigma one, undivided; fruit fleshy and indehiscent. Shrubs; with entire leaves and no stipules.

Santalaceæ.—Perianth in three or five, valvate in bud and adnate with ovary; stamens three or five, opposite to the perianth segments; ovary inferior, single-celled, with one or more ovules pendulous from near the top of a free central placenta. Leaves entire, alternate, and without stipules.

Aristolochiaceæ.—Perianth in three, tubular, often with a dilated limb, free, and adnate with ovary; stamens six to twelve, epigynous; ovary inferior, three to six-celled, with numerous ovules; style simple; stigma rayed; fruit, a six-locular capsule or berry. Climbing shrubs or low herbs; with alternate leaves, and the wood without concentric zones.

PLANTS WANTING BOTH COROLLA AND CALYX—

Empetraceæ.—Perianth of four to six hypogynous scales in two rows; stamens two or three, alternate with the inner row of scales; ovary free, on a fleshy disk. Low, shrubby, diœcious evergreens, heath-like in aspect, with alternate leaves.

Euphorbiaceæ.—Perianth three or four-lobed, or wanting; stamens one, or more than eight; capsules bursting elastically. Diœcious herbs with milky stems and entire leaves; flowers often in an involucre.

Urticaceæ.—Perianth four or five, or wanting, regular, free from the ovary; stamens four or five, hypogynous and uncoiling elastically; ovary free, single-celled. Unisexual herbs; leaves with stipules, often stinging and sometimes milky.

Ulmaceæ.—Perianth in three to eight parts, generally in five; segments imbricate in bud; stamens five, opposite segments of perianth, and inserted into its base; anthers two-celled; ovary free; stigmas two, distinct and elongated. Leaves scabious, lop-sided, distichous and stipuled; flowers perfect; fruit winged.

Cupuliferæ.—Perianth in five or six; stamens five to twenty, inserted into the base of the scales on a membranous perianth. Trees or shrubs; leaves alternate, simple, often with straight veins from mid-rib to margin; flowers in catkins; fruit in a cup.

PLANTS WANTING BOTH COROLLA AND CALYX—*(continued)*.

Betulaceæ.—Perianth in four or wanting; stamens four, opposite each division of the perianth; filaments very short and distinct; style none; stigmas two, threadlike; fruit small, double seeded, indehiscent. Trees or shrubs; leaves alternate and simple, often with veins running straight from mid-rib to margin; flowers in catkins; fruit not in a cup.

Salicaceæ.—Perianth none; stamens two to thirty; style one or none; stigmas two, entire or cleft; fruit leathery and many-seeded. Trees; leaves alternate and simple; flowers in catkins; fruit not in a cup.

Myricaceæ.—Perianth none; stamens two to eight; anthers two or four-celled, opening longitudinally; ovary free and single-celled. Aromatic shrubs; leaves alternate; flowers in catkins; fruit a drupe.

Coniferæ.—Male flowers in catkins; female flowers in cones. Trees or shrubs; leaves with parallel veins, linear, rigid, and evergreen.

MONOCOTYLEDONES.
  1. Petaloidæ.
  2. Glumiferæ.
    PETALOIDÆ.
      Ovary inferior.
      Ovary superior.
        Ovary inferior—
          Orchidaceæ.—Perianth of six segments in two rows, and irregular in shape; stamens three, one or two of which are generally abortive; stamens and style united; ovary single-celled and adnate with the perianth tube. Herbaceous plants with knob-like roots; leaves with parallel veins.
          Iridaceæ.—Perianth in six, convolute in bud in two circles; stamens three, superposed to the outer segments of the perianth; style one; stigmas three, often petaloid; ovary three-celled, adnate with the perianth tube; fruit capsular, three-valved. Leaves parallel-veined and usually equitant in two ranks; flowers spathaceous.
          Amaryllidaceæ.—Perianth in six; stamens six, inserted at the base of the perianth segments; anthers opening inwards; ovary three-celled, adnate with perianth tube; fruit capsular and three-valved. Scape-bearing herbs with bulbous roots; leaves flat, fleshy, parallel-veined, and all radical.
          Hydrocharidaceæ.—Perianth in six, three herbaceous and three petaloid, the latter occasionally wanting; stamens three or six, free from style; ovary adnate to perianth; ovary one, three, or six-celled; fruit a berry. Water plants; leaves floating or submerged, radical and with serrated margins.
          Dioscoreaceæ.—Perianth in six; stamens six from the base of the perianth; stamens and pistils in separate flowers; style deeply trifid; ovary three-celled, adnate with perianth tube; fruit a berry. Climbing plants; leaves netted-veined, cordate, stalked, and alternate; flowers small, bracteated, and in racemes.

PETALOIDÆ—(*continued*).

Ovary superior—

Liliaceæ.—Perianth of six parts in two circles; stamens six; anthers opening inwards; fruit loculicidal; ovary free from perianth. Leaves parallel-veined, narrow, sheathing, and never articulated with the stem.

Trilliaceæ.—Perianth in six or ten, in two rows, the outer herbaceous, the inner filiform; stamens six or ten; fruit a berry. Leaves ovate, with netted veins, and whorled.

Melanthaceæ.—Perianth in six, or tubular by cohesion of the segment claws; stamens six; anthers opening outwards; fruit septicidal; ovary free from perianth. Herbs; occasionally with bulbous roots; leaves linear, parallel-veined, and sheathing at the base.

Alismaceæ.—Perianth in six; stamens six; ovary free from perianth; fruit of many carpels. Water plants with broad netted-veined, radical leaves.

Naiadaceæ.—Perianth of three or four scales or wanting; stamens four; fruit of four carpels or less. Immersed aquatic plants with jointed stems, parallel-veined leaves, and sheathing stipules.

Lemnaceæ.—Perianth wanting; stamens one or two. Small, stemless, free floating plants; with cellular netted-veined leaves and axillary flowers.

Araceæ.—Perianth wanting; stamens indefinite; seeds pulpy. Leaves sheathing at the base, convolute in æstivation and often with branching veins; flowers on a spadix, enclosed in a leafy sheath.

Typhaceæ.—Perianth wanting; stamens many; seed solitary and pendulous. Marsh herbs; stems without nodes; leaves sessile, parallel-veined, and ensiform; flowers in dense conspicuous heads.

Restiaceæ.—Perianth in two or six; stamens two or three, adherent to the inner perianth segments; ovule solitary and pendulous. Aquatic herbs; stems generally with sheaths split at the side; leaves parallel-veined, but generally imperfect; flowers separated by bracts.

Juncaceæ.—Perianth in six, scarious; stamens three or six; stigmas three, sometimes one. Rushes with parallel-veined, round leaves, or leafless.

GLUMIFERÆ.

Cyperaceæ.—Stamens one to twelve. Solid stems often angular and frequently without joints; leaves with entire sheaths.

Gramineæ.—Stamens one to six, generally three. Hollow stems, jointed and sometimes branched; leaves with split sheaths.

CRYPTOGAMIA.

Cormophyta.

Thallophyta.

CORMOPHYTA.

1. Vascularia.

2. Muscineæ.

VASCULARIA.

Filices.—Leafy plants of varied structure; fructification consisting of seeds or sporules, included in capsules, thecæ or sporangia, either naked or covered with a membrane, and generally gathered in clusters on the edge or back of the leaves.

Lycopodiaceæ.—Leafy plants; fructification sessile in the axils of leaves or in the bracts of a cone.

Marsileaceæ.—Plants rooting in moist earth; slender circinate leaves; sori bisexual; spores in globular masses at the leaf bases, invested by hardened mucilage.

Equisetaceæ.—Herbaceous plants with jointed, furrowed, hollow stems, and whorls of scale-like leaves at the joints; spores on metamorphosed leaf-bearing stems.

MUSCINEÆ.

The mosses and liverworts.

THALLOPHYTA.

The Algæ, Fungi, and Protophytes—not included in the scheme of this book.

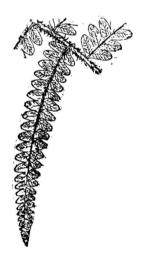

517.

CHAPTER V.

EXAMPLES OF IDENTIFICATION.

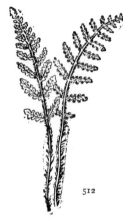

512

WE traced our plant through the orders till we identified it as one of the Ranunculaceæ, and a reference to the "Index to the Orders" will confirm us in our opinion. But to what genus of the Ranunculaceæ does it belong? We refer to the "Index to the Genera," and find that it cannot but be one of the genus Ranunculus. But to what species of Ranunculus does it belong? We refer to the "Index to the Species."

We have seen that it has a smooth round flower stalk and a spreading calyx. There is only one Ranunculus that answers to this description, and our plant is therefore *R. acris,* the kingcup, buttercup, or upright crowfoot.

But let us sort out the order Ranunculaceæ, and see on what small differences its divisions depend.

Had the beak of our plant's achene been just half as long as the rest of the carpel, and the stem of the plant had the hairs pressed close to it, we should have called it the variety *R. rectus.* Had the stem been densely hairy at the base, the achene beak shorter, and the segments of the lower leaves overlapping, the plant would have been the variety *R. vulgatus.* Had the segments of the root-leaves not overlapped, and had the points of the carpel disappeared when ripe, the plant would be *R. steveni.* The creeping or meadow crowfoot, *R. repens,* is not unlike *R. acris;* but instead of standing bolt upright, it has a creeping stem, the leaves are smaller, triangular in outline, and split into three, and, above all, the flower-stalk is furrowed. The bulbous buttercup, *R. bulbosus,* has also a channelled flower-stalk; it is a much hairier plant than *R. repens,* and has its stem thickened out at the base into a bulb or corm-like process which is peculiar to it: its leaves are of a particularly lively green, and the flowers are generally of a richer colour than those of *R. acris* or *R. repens;* it also differs from these in having a much thicker stem, and—a very important particular—its sepals, instead of following the rise of the petals, curve away from them and point downwards; in this respect it is similar to *R. hirsutus,* the hairy crowfoot, which it somewhat resembles in general appearance, the points in which the hairy crowfoot differs from it being the absence of the bulb, the paler yellow of the flowers, the rounded as against the bi-lobed shape of the petals, and the rough as against the smooth achenes. Another of the buttercups having smooth achenes and divided leaves is *R. auricomus,* the wood crowfoot, sweet-wood crowfoot, or goldilocks, whose smooth-leaved tufts form such prominent patches in our woodlands and thickets. In *R. auricomus* we have the petals frequently unequal in size and occasionally wanting altogether; its radical leaves have long stalks and are kidney or fan-shaped, and are cut into threes, while the leaves farther up the stem have no stalk to speak of, and are gashed deeply down into almost linear segments. The last of the buttercups with smooth achenes is *R. sceleratus*, the celery-leaved or cursed crowfoot, which is as common with us as it is with the Asiatics and Americans, and which seems sadly in want of some one to say a good word for it. This, the largest but one of the family, is too well known to need full description, its oblong-headed fruits being plentifully conspicuous in almost every ditch in our island, while its shiny green celery-shaped leaves, its hollow furrowed branched stem, at times as thick as a man's finger, and the long petals of its quarter-inch flowers, whose sepals turn slightly back and so bring the green centre well into prominence, have been gathered by every one of us, to be thrown away again immediately. The small-flowered crowfoot, *R. parviflorus*, has a very weak hairy stem, and the leaves are three-lobed and nearly round; the blooms are very tiny; it grows principally in corn-fields like *R. arvensis*, the corn crowfoot, which is very like it, but has its leaves deeply cut into narrow segments, has very prickly carpels, known to the children as "hedgehogs," and has a bloom of either very pale yellow or very deep orange.

All these buttercups have divided leaves, but there are a great many plants that belong to the same genus which have entire leaves, and yet could hardly be taken for anything else than ranunculi. Of these are the two spearworts, the lesser and the greater, *R. flammula* and *R. lingua*. *R. lingua* is the largest buttercup we have, and with its long lance-shaped, saw edged, almost parallel-veined sessile leaves clasping the stout hollow stem, makes a brave show in the marshy ground. Its flowers of deep bright glowing yellow, about an inch in diameter, grow in a loose cluster, known as a panicle. The lesser spearwort has narrower leaves, toothed like those of *R. lingua*, but not so deeply; at times, indeed, the denticulation is very faint. The higher the leaves the narrower and smoother they get; they are quite silky, and, unlike those of *R. lingua*, are slightly stalked. The carpels of the lesser spearwort are pitted and pointed; those of the greater spearwort are short, broad, and flat, and have a sword-shaped beak. *R. flammula* rarely exceeds a foot in height; *R. lingua* may reach four feet. The only difference between *R. flammula* and *R. reptans* is that in the latter the leaves are much narrower, almost hair-like, in fact; and while *R. flammula* does not root at the stem-joints, *R. reptans* does. In the adder's tongue crowfoot, *R. ophioglossifolius*, we have a short, sturdy plant, with insignificant flowers, heart-shaped leaves at its base, and tongue-shaped leaves higher up the stem.

In *R. ficaria*, the lesser celandine, celandine crowfoot, pilewort, or figwort, we have another buttercup with heart-shaped leaves, but differing in many respects from those of which we have been speaking. It blooms a month or two earlier than the others, and its flowers have from eight to twelve petals, and are of a bright metallic-looking yellow; it has only three sepals, and the stalk is only one-flowered;

it is of low growth, and rarely has more than half a dozen blossoms, which shine out like stars against its glossy dark green and frequently black-spotted leaves; its roots are knobbed and fig-shaped; when the leaves do not overlap at its base, the plant is sometimes called *R. divergens;* when they do overlap, it is known as *R. incumbens.* It is only during the last few years that *R. ficaria, R. divergens,* and *R. incumbens* have been classified as ranunculi.

From the land we must now take to the water, for there are water ranunculi as well as land ones, and the commonest aquatic plants we have will, on examination, be found to resemble those we have been describing. There is one important difference—easy to remember— the land crowfoots are all yellow, the water crowfoots all white. It is very difficult to accurately determine these water crowfoots unless we are satisfied to call them all *R. aquatilis.* The distinctions depend almost entirely on the shape of the leaves, and their shape varies with the condition of the water and the work they have to do. There are two kinds of these leaves—the floating and the submerged, and the latter are in different stages of thread-like subdivision. The flowers grow each on a stalk, are five-petalled and white, and the petals have no scale at the base. If the flowers are about three-quarters of an inch in diameter, and the plant has both kinds of leaves, and the submerged leaves collapse into a pencil when taken from the water, the plant, if found in a pond, will be *R. heterophyllus,* the mallow-leaved crowfoot; if found in a stream, it will be *R. pseudo-fluitans.* Should the under leaves not collapse, and the carpels be blunt, the plant will be either *R. peltatus* or *R. floribundus; R. peltatus* if the upper leaves are clover-shaped, and the flower is sweet scented; *R. floribundus* if the clover-like leaf is toothed. Should the carpels be narrow the plant will be *R. baudotii,* if the stamens are shorter than the pistil; *R. confusus,* if the pistil is shorter than the stamens. These four varieties will be found in ponds or ditches. In a swiftly-flowing stream there will be found two varieties with no floating leaves at all. One of these, *R. fluitans,* the real river or floating water crowfoot, has its submerged leaves narrowly wedge-shaped, and divided into long rigid, almost parallel segments; its flower-stalks are much shorter than the leaves. The other is *R. bachii,* and it has a very slender stem, much shorter leaves, and much longer flower-stalks. All the large-flowered water crowfoots must belong to one of these six groups; but the collector need not sorrow much if, like other people, he is unable to say which.

There are three small-flowered white ranunculi which have no floating leaves. One of these, *R. drouetii,* collapses when taken from the water, while the other two spread. *R. drouetii* has wedge-shaped leaves something like those of the maidenhair fern, and each wedge has four teeth along its base. The two non-collapsing varieties are *R. tricophyllus* and *R. circinatus,* the water-fennel or hairy-leaved water crowfoot, and the rigid-leaved water crowfoot. The leaves of *R. circinatus* spread out in one plane like a fan, often grow at right angles to the stem, and may run up to an inch in diameter; the leaves of the water-fennel spread out all round like a broom and grow in threes and twos.

Some of these water crowfoots have no submerged leaves. *R. tripartitus* has leaves of the *R. drouetii* shape, but having three wedges all above water, whereas *R. drouetii* has but one, and that below water. Next we have the mud crowfoot, *R. lenormandi*—a well-known ditch plant, with large almost round alternate leaves, heart shaped at the base, and edged with brown—which never floats but creeps in the mud ; and then we reach the last of the white ranunculi, the ivy-leaved crowfoot, *R. hederaceus*, which has rounded broad-lobed leaves much like those of *R. lenormandi*, only they are opposite instead of alternate, and it has a smaller bloom. We have thus exhausted the genus *Ranunculus*, and the plants described have all these common characteristics. The flowers, either yellow or white, have generally five sepals and five petals each with a thickened hollow spot at the base. The carpels are contained in an oblong or globular head ; the stamens are always numerous.

Myosurus minimus, the little mouse-tail, belongs to a different genus, and, unlike every other plant in the tribe, has only five stamens. Its pale greenish-yellow flowers have five sepals and five petals with small linear tubular claws which grow round an elongated spike of carpels rising from the centre like a little green tail. But for its insignificance, the mouse-tail would long ago have had an order of its own.

A plant resembling a buttercup in everything but colour is the pheasant's eye, red maithes, red morocco, flos adonis, or *Adonis autumnalis*. It has scarlet petals varying from five to ten in number, hollow and black at the base, and having no nectary. The sepals are pink, and when in the bud are imbricate, or overlap like roofing tiles, and the leaves are much divided and grow on a furrowed stem.

Up to the present we have found in our flowers both sepals and petals ; but there are a great many plants belonging to this tribe which have no petals. The corolla is abortive and absent, but in its stead is a brilliantly-coloured calyx. This is very apparent with *Caltha palustris*, the marsh marigold, Mary's gold, water blob, mary-bud, water caltrops, or meadow rout. At first sight it looks like a fine, rich, handsome yellow buttercup, and so it is. But it is a butter-cup without petals. The corolla is not there, and the five or six leaves which form the coloured envelope are those of the calyx. This bright flower can rarely be mistaken, as it glows like a golden star in its marshy home, relieved by its background of dark, kidney-shaped leaves. The sepals in *C. palustris* overlap slightly, in *C. guerangerii* they stand apart ; the flower, too, is slightly smaller. *C. vulgaris* differs from *C. guerangerii* in having a larger flower, sometimes two inches across, and short beaks to its carpels. *C. minor* bears the smallest of these blossoms. It has only one flower on a stem, and the sepals are oval and open so as not to touch. Like *C. vulgaris* it has carpels with a very short beak. All these marigolds have upright stems, that of *C. minor* being the weakest ; but in *C. radicans* we have one with a creeping stem rooting at the joints. Its sepals gape very much, and its leaves form a much more obtuse angle than those of the rest, and are toothed.

Another flower in which the corolla is absent is the anemone of which there are four species. The yellow or crowfoot anemone, *Anemone ranunculoides*, with its five elliptic sepals, is at first sight not unlike the marigold, but close up underneath the flower there will be seen a collar or involucre of three deeply-cut leaves. The peduncle or flower-stalk will be seen to taper downwards, so that its

E

greatest girth is at this involucre. The commonest of the anemones is the wood anemone or wind flower, *A. nemorosa*, one of the freshest and fairest of our spring blossoms. It differs from *A. ranunculoides* in having six sepals beautifully smooth. The flower is about an inch and a quarter across, white, and daintily tinged with pink, and it droops some distance above the involucre. The deeply-gashed leaves are wedge-like in form, and of a dark green. *A. apennina*, the mountain anemone, is a bright blue star-shaped flower with yellow anthers and a green centre, sometimes having as many as twelve sepals. The pasque flower anemone or Easter flower, *A. pulsatilla*, is much more delicately made. It has six silky purple sepals, which open out fully only in the sun. Its leaves are not so much branched as those of its sisters. The rootstock of *A. pulsatilla* is thick and woody, that of *A. nemorosa* quite black and horizontal, and of the four anemones, *A. nemorosa*, has the darkest coloured leaves. They all have the three-leaved involucre, the tapering stem, short stamens, and many carpels.

The meadow rues are all small. Like caltha and anemone, they have no petals, but they are yellowish in bloom, have all yellow roots and give a yellow dye. The brightest of them is *Thalictrum alpinum*, the poor man's rhubarb cr alpine meadow rue, which is rarely above six inches high. The sepals in all the meadow rues are very narrow, and either four or five in number, and they overlap each other so that the bloom is cup-shaped. The stem is simple, green, and bare. *T. minus*, the lesser meadow rue, has a leafy zigzag stem bent at every node. The flowers of *T. alpinum* grow in a cluster on an unbranched peduncle, or in a raceme, as it is called. In *T. minus* they grow in a loose, irregular panicle ; in other words, the flower-stalk is branched.

There are several varieties of *T. minus*. *T. maritimum* and *T. montanum*, the sea and mountain meadow rues, have their stem leaves confined to the upper part. The stem of *T. maritimum* is purple and the flower of an orange hue. The flowers of *T. montanum* are purplish and much larger than those of *T. maritimum*, and its leaves are a glaucous green. The other varieties have the leaves at the base of the stem. A large variety, almost a purely North of England one, which may reach five feet in height, and has very large leaflets and a leafy panicle, is *T. flexuosum*. Koch's meadow rue, *T. kochii* a lake district variety, has the leafy stem, but the flowers are very straggling, and the leaves are small and very like dark green shamrocks. The stone meadow rue, *T. saxatile*, is a sturdier plant with smaller, slenderer, lighter green leaves and an angled stem. The common meadow rue, *T. flavum*, has a more creeping rootstock and a deeply-furrowed stem, sturdy, erect, and well branched, frequently attaining four feet in height. The leaves are large and of a deep green, and the flowers are in a compact panicle. In *T. sphæro-carpum*, so called because of its globular achenes, the panicle of bloom is more contracted. In *T. riparium*, which has ovoid achenes, the panicle is very loose, while *T. morisonii* has oblong achenes, and a panicle made up of small bundles of flowers. All the typical meadow rues are yellow, but *T. minus* and its varieties are very greenish in tint and frequently darken into reds and purples, while *T. flavum* and its varieties are much paler, and often lighten into pinks and creams. The stamens are always brilliantly yellow.

We now reach the last petalless crowfoot, and it may be rather start-ling to find that this is none other than the climbing clematis. Unlike the rest of the tribe it has a woody stem, and, like *Ranunculus hedera-ceus* alone, it has opposite leaves, but in all other particulars it has the true characteristics. It is the only climbing crowfoot, and has a genus to itself. *Clematis vitalba*, the traveller's joy, old man's beard, virgin's bower, smoke wood, wood-vine, is hardly likely to be mistaken for any other plant, its leaves going off at right angles to the stem, which will sometimes be yards in length and as thick as a man's wrist. Its small, many-stamened, starlikeflowers of greenish white springing from the leaf junctions or axils, and the delicate bunches of down formed by the long feathery tails which terminate the carpels are to be found on every hedge and in nearly every woodland on a limestone soil.

Let us now go back to the marsh marigold, whose flower consisted, as we saw, of five bright yellow sepals. Let those five sepals curl up over the missing five petals, which you can increase to any number up to fifteen, and make as short and as narrow as you please, and you have the globular ranunculus, the *Trollius europæus* or globe flower, the leaves of which are divided into three or four segments, and in shape resemble those of thalictrum. Let the sepals be but five in number, smaller and flatter, and drop off as the flower ages, and add a leafy involucre like a little boy's frill, and you have the early-blooming winter aconite, *Eranthis hyemalis*, whose glossy, long-stalked radical leaves are frequently found in our gardens. Let the five sepals be green or purple and remain throughout, and let the small petals be either eight, nine, or ten, and tubular and two-lipped, and you have one of the hellebores. *Helleborus viridis*, the green hellebore, has its green calyx well open, and the radical leaves well divided into lance-shaped segments ; *H. fœtidus*, the stinking helle-bore or bear's-foot, has its purple calyx convergent, and the leaves but slightly nicked into the paw-shape, from which it takes its trivial name. The leaves, too, of *H. fœtidus* are evergreen, those of *H. viridis* are deciduous, that is, fall off during the winter.

The well-known white herb-christopher, or baneberry, *Actæa spicata*, is very like thalictrum in habit. It can easily be identified by its triangular stems and the elder-shaped leaves after which it is called. Its sepals and petals are generally four each in number, but the sepals may vary from three to five, and the petals may range up to ten. The calyx disappearing very early in the flower's life, the plant is usually recognised by its corolla or its black oval berries. Another of the group not far removed from actæa is the pœony, *Pæonia corallina*, which usually has the five sepals, five petals, and five carpels, and whose bright red blooms, four inches across, with their pistils covered with whitish wool and ringed with yellow stamens, are seen in such profusion and guarded so jealously in Steep-Holme Island in the Bristol Channel, but which we have not included in our lists, owing to the doubt that exists as to its being a native.

And now we come to a flower which differs from all other British flowers, and once seen can never be mistaken. This is the columbine, *Aquilegia vulgaris*, whose five petals, each curved back into a graceful spur, look like five tiny turtle-doves just settling round a vase. Purple, pink, or white, it is the gem of many a thicket in May or June. It is a true ranunculus—sepals five, petals five, carpels five, and stamens many.

Hitherto we have been dealing with flowers that are regular, that is, have their sepals or petals of equal length ; but before we end with the plants of which the crowfoot is the type, we have two to deal with, two whose flowers are irregular or lop-sided. The first of these is the larkspur, *Delphinium ajacis*, which has five blue sepals, two of which are produced backwards into a spur as long as the rest of the flower, and four petals, two of which are united on the under side into an inner spur which is open along its upper edge. The other is *Aconitum napellus*, the monkshood, aconite, or wolfsbane, which, instead of having its sepals and petals spurred, has them helmet-shaped or hooded.

In appearance the wolfsbane differs more than any flower we have yet dealt with from our typical buttercup, and it will perhaps be as well to take it to pieces, as we did the crowfoot, to discover the resemblance. In the buttercup we had the calyx of five separate sepals, and the corolla of five golden petals circling round the stamens and the pistil. Pulling off the outer envelope of the wolfsbane, we find that the dark blue, queerly-shaped sepals are still five in number. The upper one is the big cowl, the monk's hood ; on each side of it come two broad, flat, straight ears, and below them are the two other sepals, small and narrow. When the sepals are off we shall find the much-modified petals ; two of them are sure to be there, but the other three will probably be modified out of existence. The two horns with the honey cup at the bottom are the petals. The stamens are there in their proper abundance, the carpels are there, but only three of them.

The aconite is cross-fertilized, and like all the rest of the cross-fertilized flowers the development of its shape is due to the fact that each accidental peculiarity ensuring easier fertilization by its special insect visitor has been perpetuated and accentuated. In all the flowers we have passed in review we can trace the same influence. " The simplest kinds," says Mr. Grant Allen in his admirable paper on the monkshood, " are round, yellow, and many-carpelled, like the buttercups. These three species which display their sepals largely have dwarfed petals, like hellebore and globe flower, or have lost them altogether like marsh marigold, which trusts entirely for colour display to its big golden calyx. The still higher anemones have the sepals white, red, or blue ; and the very advanced columbine has all the petals spurred, and developed into nectaries like those of monkshood. But columbine still keeps to single terminal flowers, so that here the five petals remain regular and circularly symmetrical, though the carpels are reduced to five. Fancy a number of such columbine flowers crowded together on a spike, however, and you can readily picture to yourself by rough analogy the origin of monkshood. The sepals would now become the most conspicuous part ; the two upper petals would alone be useful in insuring fertilization, and the lower ones would soon shrivel away from pure disuse. The development of the hood and the lengthening of the upper petals would easily follow by insect selection. It is a significant fact that our only other spiked buttercup, the larkspur, has equally irregular and bilateral flowers, though its honey is concealed in a long spur formed by the petals, and accessible to but one English insect, the humble bee."

And now to sum up. We have been dealing in this chapter with the great natural order of the Ranunculaceæ. We have rapidly surveyed all the plants by which that order is represented in our British flora. We have seen that, with one exception, they none of them have less than a dozen stamens, that they generally have five or more petals, and five or more sepals, that their fruit consists of many distinct carpels or single-seeded achenes, and that with two exceptions they have regular flowers. Those two exceptions are each represented by a minor division, family, or genus, and we have shown how one of them differs from the other, the genus delphinium being distinguished by its irregular spur, the genus aconitum by its irregular hood. We have found the order represented by twelve genera other than these, all with regular blooms ; and we have seen how clematis, thalictrum, anemone, and caltha have no petals, while the others have. We have distinguished the tailed and climbing clematis from the tailless thalic-trum, and the bare and brilliant caltha from the involucred anemone. The eight remaining genera, in which the flower appears in its complete form with calyx and corolla, have also been briefly contrasted. We have dealt in detail with the type genus ranunculus in both its land and water developments. We have compared the scarlet adonis with the brown-tailed myosurus, the globes of trollius with the frilled chalices of eranthis, the insect-trapping helleborus with the dove-like aquilegia, the woolly-centred pæonia with the berried actæa. Where these genera have been divided into species, we have dealt with those species, and where the species have been subdivided into varieties, we have dealt with those varieties in order to show that of species making there need be no end if the mania meets with encouragement. But in our lists we have taken no notice of mere varieties, and have included only such species as are generally recognised as natives of Britain.

There is no need for us to go through order after order in the same detail as we have done in the case of the Ranunculaceæ. A reference first to the tabular system of orders, then to the index of genera, and then to the index of species, will enable the student to name any plant in our island flora.

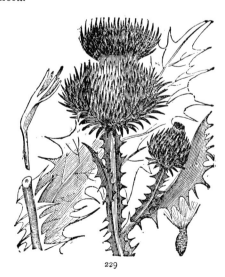

229

One other example will suffice. To what order does this plant belong? There are only two within the bounds of possibility. One of these is *Dipsaceæ*, the other *Compositæ;* but the absence of a calyx and the presence of the four stamens instead of five, to say nothing of other characteristics, at once give the verdict in favour of the *Compositæ*. What genus then of the *Compositæ* is here represented? Let us turn to the index. Here Division D at once puts us on the track. "Florets all tubular, the style thickened below its branches as in the thistle." Division D is divided into plants with smooth leaves, and plants with spiny leaves; and as our plant has most unmistakably spiny leaves, we look for its genus in the second series of our D. division. In this there are only three genera, *Carduus*, *Carlina*, and *Onopordum*. In *Carlina* we read the inner row of bracts is chaffy and straw-coloured, which is certainly not the case in our plant. It is, therefore, either a *Carduus* or an *Onopordum;* but the fruit of *Carduus* is flat, while that of the plant we have has four ribs, so that we are evidently dealing with *Onopordum*, and our identification is confirmed by the erect branched stem, the spinous wings and the leaves woolly on both sides. Our plant is obviously, *Onopordum acanthium,* the Scotch or cotton thistle.

18

CHAPTER VI.

GLOSSARY.

THE following dictionary of terms contains many more than those used in this book, so that it may prove of value to students desirous of advancing beyond the mere "nodding acquaintance" stage of our country's flowers.

516

Abrupt—suddenly terminating. **Abruptly pinnate**—pinnate without a terminal leaflet.
Acaulescent—seemingly without a stem. **Accessory**—extra or additional.
Accrescent—increasing in size after flowering. **Accumbent**—lying against.
Acerose—rather acicular. **Acetabuliform**—saucer-shaped.
Achene—a dry, single-seeded fruit, with a separable pericarp.
Achlamydeous—without calyx and corolla. **Acicular**—needle-shaped.
Acotyledonous—without seed leaves. **Acrogenous**—growing from the apex.
Aculeate—prickly. **Aculeolate**—rather prickly.
Acuminate—with a tapering point. **Adnate**—adherent to from the first.
Adpressed—touching but not united. **Adventitious**—growing in an unusual position.
Æstivation—arrangement of the flower when in the bud.
Ala—the wing petal of a papilionaceous flower.
Alate—winged, as in the fruit of acer. **Albescent**—whitish.
Albumen—the food stored up with the embryo. **Alburnum**—young, or sap, wood.
Alternate—standing over the intervals between the pair beneath.
Alveolate—honeycombed. **Amentiferous**—bearing catkins.
Amplexicaul—embracing the stem. **Ampullaceous**—distended like a bottle.
Anastomosing—forming a net-work.
Ancipital—double-edged. **Andræcium**—the whole of the stamens.
Androgynous—having both staminate and pistillate flowers in the same cluster.
Androphore—a column of united stamens.
Angiospermous—having the seeds formed in an ovary.
Annual—coming into life and blooming and dying all in the year.
Annular—in a ring shape. **Anterior**—external.
Anther—the head of the stamen. **Antrorse**—growing upwards or forwards.
Apetalous—without petals. **Aphyllous**—without foliage.
Apocarpous—having the pistils separate. **Apophysis**—any irregular enlargement
Apothecia—the peltate disks on the surface of lichens. **Appressed**—closely squeezed.
Apterous—wingless. **Arachnoid**—like a cobweb.
Arborescent—like a tree. **Arcuate**—bent like a bow.
Arillus—an extra coat on the seed due to the expansion of the placenta after the ovule is fertilised.
Aristate—furnished with bristles. **Articulated**—jointed.
Auriculate—with ear-shaped appendages. **Awn**—a bristle.
Axil—the angle made by the upper side of the leaf with the stem.

Axillary—growing in the axil.   **Axis**—the root and stem together.
Baccate—like a berry.   **Barbate**—bearded.
Basal—belonging to the base.   **Beak**—a long narrow tip.
Bicarinate—double keeled.   **Bidentate**—having two teeth.
Biennial—coming into life one year and blooming and dying the next.
Bifid—cleft in two.   **Bifoliate**—having two leaflets.
Bijugate—having two pairs of leaflets.   **Bilabiate**—having two lips.
Bilamellate—having two plates.   **Bilocular**—having two cells.
Bipinnate—doubly pinnate.   **Bipinnatifid**—doubly pinnatifid.
Brachiate—having the opposite branches at right angles.
Bract—the leaf or scale from the axil of which the flower bud grows.
Bractlet—an intermediate leaf between the bract and the calyx.
Bulb—a leaf-bud with fleshy scales from the under surface of which roots grow down.
Bulbil—an axillary bulb produced by some of the lilies.
Bullate—like a bladder.
Caducous—falling very early.   **Cæspitose**—growing in tufts.
Calcarate—having a spur.   **Calceolate**—shaped like a slipper.
Callosity—a thickened spot.   **Calyptra**—the hood of a moss capsule.
Calyx—the outer whorl of the floral envelopes.
Cambium—the layer of mucilage between the wood and the bark.
Campanulate—shaped like a bell.
Campylospermous—having the seed curved at the edges.
Canaliculate—channelled.   **Cancellate**—like lattice work.
Canescent—hoary.   **Capillary**—like hair.
Capitate—having a globular head.
Capitulum—a group of flowers on a nearly flat receptacle.   **Capreolate**—tendrilled.
Capsule—a dry seed vessel opening by valves or pores.   **Carina**—a keel.
Carpel—the modified leaves forming the pistil.
Carpophore—an extension of the thalamus forming the stalk of the fruit or pistil within the flower.
Caruncle—an excrescence at the scar of a seed.
Catkin—a scaly deciduous spike of flowers.   **Caudate**—tailed.
Caudex—an upright rootstock.   **Caulescent**—having a stem.
Caulicle—a small stem.   **Cernuous**—nodding.
Chalaza—the point of union in the ovule betwen the base of the nucleus and the integuments.
Channelled—grooved.   **Chlorophyll**—the green colouring matter of the plant.
Ciliate—having the margin fringed with hairs.   **Cinereous**—the colour of ashes.
Circinate—rolled up like a crosier.   **Cirrhose**—like a tendril.
Clathrate—like lattice work.   **Clavate**—club-shaped.
Claw—the narrow base of a petal.   **Clypeate**—buckler-shaped.
Coalescent—growing together.   **Cochleate**—coiled like a snail shell.
Cœlopermous—having the seed hollowed on the inner face.
Collum—the point of junction between stem and root.
Columella—the axis to which the carpels of a compound pistil are attached.
Column—the united stamens, or the stamens and pistils united into one mass.
Comose—tufted.   **Commissure**—the junction line between the carpels.
Compound leaf—a leaf divided down to the mid-rib into leaflets.
Compressed—flattened on opposite sides.   **Conduplicate**—folded in half lengthwise.
Confluent—grown together.   **Conjugate**—coupled.
Connate—joined together from the first.
Connective—the part of the anther uniting its lobes.   **Connivent**—converging.
Convolute—rolled up lengthwise.   **Cordate**—heart-shaped.
Coriaceous—leathery.   **Corm**—an expansion of the base of the stem.
Corneous—horny.   **Corolla**—the inner whorl of floral envelopes.
Cortex—the bark.
Corymb—having the pedicels so arranged that the flowers are all on the same level.
Cotyledon—the first leaf of the embryo.   **Crateriform**—shaped like a goblet.
Crenate—having the edge cut into rounded teeth.
Cruciform—in the form of a cross.   **Crustaceous**—hard and brittle.
Cryptogam—a flowerless plant.   **Cucullate**—hood-shaped.

Culm—the stem of a grass or sedge.   **Cuneate**—wedge-shaped.
Cupule—a small cup.   **Cuspidate**—sharply pointed.
Cuticle—the external pellicle of the skin of plants.
Cyme—a corymb with the blossoms from terminal buds.
Deciduous—falling off.   **Decompound**—much divided.
Decumbent—lying on the ground at the base.
Decurrent—prolonged on the stem so as to form a border.
Decussate—arranged in pairs alternately crossing.
Dehiscence—the manner in which a pod, or anther, sheds its contents.
Dentate—toothed.   **Denticulate**—having very small teeth.
Depressed—flattened vertically.   **Dextrorse**—turned to the right hand.
Diadelphous—united in two groups.   **Diandrous**—having two stamens.
Diagnosis—a brief distinguishing description.   **Diaphanous**—translucent.
Dichlamydeous—having both calyx and corolla.
Dichotomous—having two forks.
Diclinous—having the stamens in one flower and the pistils in another.
Dicotyledonous—having two seed leaves.
Didynamous—having four stamens in two pairs, with one pair shorter than the other.
Digitate—having the leaflets all on the top of the stalk.
Digynous—with two pistils.
Diœcious—having the stamens and pistils in separate flowers, and on different plants.
Drupe—a fruit with a stone in it.   **Duramen**—the heart wood.
Ebracteate—having no bracts.   **Echinate**—prickly.
Edentate—toothless.   **Emarginate**—notched at the summit.
Emersed—raised out of the water.   **Endocarp**—the inner layer of the fruit.
Endogens—the monocotyledons.   **Endosperm**—the albumen of a seed.
Endostome—the orifice in the inner coat of an ovule.
Ensiform—sword-shaped.   **Epicarp**—the outermost layer of a fruit.
Epigynous—upon the ovary.   **Epipetalous**—upon the petals.
Epiphyllous—upon a leaf.   **Epiphyte**—a plant growing on another, but not nourished by it
Equitant—embracing at the base.   **Etiolated**—blanched by excluding the light.
Exogens—the dicotyledons.   **Exserted**—protruding.
Exstipulate—having no stipules.   **Extrorse**—turned outwards away from the centre.
Falcate—shaped like a scythe.   **Fascicle**—a close bundle.
Fastigiate—close, parallel, and upright.   **Filament**—the stalk of the stamen.
Fistular—hollow and cylindrical.   **Floret**—one of the flowers in a compound flower.
Follicle—a simple pod opening down the inner suture.
Frond—the leaf of a fern, or the stem and leaf of a duckweed.
Fructification—the manner of fruiting.   **Fugacious**—soon falling away.
Funiculus—the foot of the seed or podosperm.   **Fusiform**—spindle shaped.
Glabrous—smooth.   **Glaucous**—pale greenish blue.
Globose—nearly spherical.   **Glume**—the floral covering of a grass.
Gymnosperms—the cone-bearing plants.
Gynandrous—having the stamens borne on the pistil.
Gynæcium—the pistils taken together.
Gynophore—the stalk raising the pistil above the stamens.
Habitat—the locality in which a plant grows in its wild state.
Hemicarp—one of the carpels of an umbellifer.   **Hemitropous**—amphitropous.
Herbaceous—not woody.   **Hermaphrodite**—having stamens and pistils in the same flower
Heterogamous—bearing different sorts of flowers.
Heterorhizal—germinating from any part of the surface.
Hilum—the point of union of the funiculus with the ovule.   **Hirsute**—with stiffish hairs.
Hispid—bristly.   **Hoary**—with greyish white down.   **Homogeneous**—all of one kind.
Homomorphous—all of one shape.   **Homotropous**—curved one way.
Hypocrateriform—salver shaped.   **Hypogynous**—inserted beneath the pistil.
Imbricate—overlapping, like the tiles of a roof.
Immarginate—without a rim.   **Immersed**—growing under water.
Incised—cut deeply and irregularly.   **Incumbent**—leaning upon.
Incurved—curving inwards.   **Indefinite**—too numerous to count easily.
Indehiscent—not splitting or bursting.   **Indigenous**—growing wild in the country.

Induplicate—with the edges turned inwards.
Indusium—the membranous scale enclosing the thecæ of ferns.   **Inflated**—bladdery.
Inflexed—bent inwards   **Inflorescence**—the manner in which the flowers are arranged.
Infundibular—funnel shaped.   **Interruptedly pinnate**—with smaller leaflets between
Introrse—facing inwards.   **Involucel**—a small involucre.   [the larger.
Involucre—the whorl of bracts.   **Involute**—rolled inwards from the edges.
Irregular—not uniform in general form.
Jagged—irregularly cut at the margin.   **Jointed**—separable into pieces.
Keel—the lower petals of a papilionaceous corolla ; a projecting ridge.
Kernel—the seed of a nut.   **Key**—a winged fruit.
Knobbed—with a globular head.
Labellum—the odd petal in the *Orchidaceæ*.
Labiate—lipped.   **Laciniate**—cut into deep narrow lobes.
Lactescent—with milky juice.   **Lacunose**—full of holes.
Lævigate—smooth as if polished.   **Lamina**—the expanded part of a petal.
Lanceolate—oblong, narrow, and tapering towards each end.
Leaflets—the divisions of a compound leaf.
Legume—a long dry seed vessel with two valves.
Lenticular—flatly convex on both sides.   **Ligneous**—woody.
Limb—the expanded part of the corolla   **Linear**—narrow and flat, with parallel margins.
Lobe—the rounded segment of a leaf.
Loculicidal—splitting down the middle of the back of the cell.
Locusta—the spikelet of the grasses.   **Loment**—a pod separating into joints transversely.
Lunate—crescent-shaped.   **Lyrate**—lyre-shaped.
Maculate—spotted.   **Marcescent**—withering without falling off.
Medullary rays—the silver grain of wood.
Mericarp—one of the carpels of the fruit of umbellifers.
Mesocarp—the middle layer of the pericarp.
Mesophlæum—the middle bark.   **Micropyle**—the closed orifice of the seed.
Monadelphous—having the stamens united by their filaments into one group.
Monandrous—having only one stamen.
Moniliform—cylindrical, but contracted at intervals.
Monochlamydeous—having either a calyx or corolla, but not both.
Monocotyledonous—having a single seed leaf.
Monœcious—when the same plant bears both male and female flowers.
Monogynous—having only one pistil or style.
Monopetalous—having the corolla undivided into petals.
Monosepalous—having the calyx undivided into sepals.
Monospermous—single-seeded.   **Mucronate**—with a short point.
Muricate—covered with short and hard points.
Nectary—the part of the flower where honey is found.
Nervation—the pattern of the leaf veins.   **Nerve**—the rib or vein of a leaf.
Netted—branched and interlacing.   **Nodose**—with knobs.
Normal—according to rule.   **Nut**—a seed covered with a hard shell which does not burst.
Oblong—three or four times as long as broad, and with rounded ends.
Obovate—broad end upwards.   **Obtuse**—rounded at the end.
Obvolute—when the margins of one leaf in the bud alternately overlap those of the
          opposite one.
Ochreate—having stipules in the form of sheaths.   **Ochroleucous**—cream coloured.
Operculate—having a lid.   **Opposite**—in pairs on opposite sides of the stem.
Ovule—the seed in its early stage.
Palea—the inner husk of a grass.   **Palmate**—having oblong segments extending to the middle.
Panduriform—fiddle-shaped.   **Panicle**—a compound raceme.
Papilionaceous—shaped like a butterfly, as the corollas of the *Leguminosæ*.
Pappus—the tuft of down on the seeds of *Compositæ*.
Parenchyma—the soft cellular tissue of plants.   **Pectinate**—like the teeth of a comb.
Pedate—like a bird's foot.   **Pedicel**—the stalk of each particular flower.
Peduncle—the stalk either of the flower or the cluster.
Peltate—shaped like a shield with the stalk in the centre.
Pendulous—hanging.   **Pentamerous**—having its parts in fives.

Pepo—a fruit like a cucumber. **Perennial**—lasting from year to year.
Perfoliate—with the stem running through the leaves.
Perianth—the floral envelopes when it is not easy to distinguish between them.
Pericarp—the envelope of the seeds. **Pericline**—the green base of the thistle bloom.
Perigone—the perianth.
Perigynous—when the stamens and the petals are borne on the calyx.
Perisperm—the albumen of a seed. **Persistent**—remaining till the fruit is ripe.
Personate—bilabiate with a palate in the throat of the corolla.
Petal—a corolla leaf. **Petiole**—the stalk of the leaf.
Phanerogamous—bearing flowers and producing seeds.
Phyllode—a leaf wherein the blade is a dilated petiole.
Phyllotaxis—the arrangement of leaves on the stem.
Pinnate—when the leaflets grow along only one stalk.
Pinnatifid—lobed after the manner of a pinnate leaf.
Pistil—the seed-bearing part of the flower.
Placenta—the part of the ovary to which the ovules are attached.
Plicate—plaited.
Podosperm—the prolongation by which the seed is attached to the placenta.
Pollen—the fertilising powder shed by the anther.
Polyadelphous—having the stamens in several bundles.
Polygamous—having some perfect and some separated flowers on the same or different plants.
Polypetalous—having separate petals. **Polysepalous**—having separate sepals.
Polyspermous—many seeded. **Pome**—a fleshy fruit like the apple.
Præmorse—bitten off. **Procumbent**—trailing on the ground.
Proliferous—where a new branch or flower cluster grows from another
Prostrate—lying on the ground. **Punctate**—dotted.
Putamen—the stone of a drupe or shell of a nut.
Quadrangular—flat and four-cornered.
Raceme—a flower cluster in which the pedicels are of equal length.
Rachis—the stem of the plant. **Radical**—apparently growing from the root.
Radicle—the stem part of the embryo.
Raphe—the process uniting the base of the nucleus with the base of the ovule.
Ray—the marginal flowers of a head of bloom.
Receptacle—the support of a head of flowers. **Recurved**—curved outwards.
Reniform—kidney shaped. **Replum**—the frame of pod.
Reticulated—resembling net-work. **Rhizome**—the rootstock.
Ringent—having the lips separated and the upper one arched. **Rotate**—wheel-shaped.
Runcinate—coarsely toothed, or pinnatifid with the teeth pointed downwards.
Sagittate—arrow-headed. **Samara**—a winged fruit.
Sap—the juice of a plant. **Scabrous**—rough to the touch.
Scalariform—like a ladder. **Scandent**—climbing.
Scape—a flower stalk rising from the root. **Scarious**—thin, dry, and membranous.
Scorpioid—circinate at the end. **Scrobiculate**—pitted.
Seminal—relating to the seed. **Septicidal**—splitting through the partitions.
Septum—a partition. **Serotinous**—happening late in the season.
Sessile—stalkless. **Setaceous**—like a bristle.
Setose—bristly. **Silicle**—a pouch or short pod.
Silique—a long pod. **Sinistrorse**—turned to the left.
Sinuate—wavy. **Soboliferous**—bearing shoots from near the ground.
Sori—the groups of capsules on a fern frond. **Spadix**—a fleshy spike of flowers.
Spathe—a bract surrounding an inflorescence.
Spathulate—circular at the end and tapering towards the base.
Spicate—in the form of a spike.
Spike—a raceme in which the flowers are without stalks.
Spikelet—the inflorescence of grasses. **Spiny**—thorny.
Sporangia—the spore cases of ferns. **Spores**—the representatives of seeds in ferns.
Spur—a projecting appendage to a flower. **Squamate**—scaly.
Squarrose—widely spreading. **Stamen**—the male organ of the flower.
Standard—the upper petal of a papilionaceous corolla. **Stigma**—the top of the style.

Stipule—an appendage at the base of a leaf. **Stolon**—a trailing shoot.

Strobile—a catkin hardened and enlarged.

Style—the part of the pistil which bears the stigma. **Suberose**—like cork.

Subulate—shaped like an awl. **Surculose**—producing suckers.

Suture—the line of junction of contiguous parts.

Symmetrical—having the number of parts all equal.

Syncarpous—having several carpels united into one.

Syngenesious—having the stamens united by their anthers.

Tail—an appendage to the seed. **Tap root**—a stout tapering root.

Tegmen—the inner coat of the seed. **Tendril**—a thread-like organ used for climbing.

Terete—long and round but not necessarily cylindrical.

Terminal—borne at the end **Ternate**—in threes.

Tetradynamous—having six stamens, two being shorter than the rest

Tetragonal—four angled. **Tetrandrous**—having four stamens.

Thalamus—the growing point of the pistil.

Thecæ—the spore cases of ferns, the sporangia.

Thyrsus—a compact panicle in which the pedicels are short and hick.

Tomentose—woolly. **Torus**—the receptacle of the flower, the thalamus.

Triadelphous—having the stamens united into three bundles.

Trichotomous—forked in threes. **Tricuspidate**—with three points.

Trifid—cleft in three. **Trifoliate**—with leaves in threes.

Trilocular—with the pistil or pod having three cells.

Tricœcious—having hree sets of flowers on the same or different plants.

Triquetrous—bayonet pointed. **Truncate**—cut off sharp at the top.

Trunk—the main stem.

Tuber—a thickened portion of a subterranean stem or branch with buds on the sides.

Tubercle—a small excrescence. **Tumid**—bulging.

Turbinate—spherical and depressed. **Turgid**—bloated.

Umbel—having the pedicels of equal length and starting from a common centre.

Umbilicate—depressed in the centre. **Umbonate**—having a rounded projection.

Unarmed—having no thorns. **Uncinate**—hooked.

Undivided—having no segments. **Undulate**—wavy.

Unguiculate—clawed. **Unilocular**—having one cell.

Unilateral—inclining all one way. **Unisexual**—having stamens or pistils only.

Urceolate —urn-shaped. **Utricle**—a dry indehiscent fruit with an inflated pericarp.

Vaginate—having a sheath. **Valvate**—opening by valves.

Veins—the framework cf leaves. **Veinlets**—the smaller veins.

Velate—having a veil. **Velutinous**—velvety.

Venation—the arrangement of the veins in the leaf.

Ventral—the side facing the centre of the flower.

Vermicular—worm-shaped. **Vernicose**—looking as if varnished.

Verrucose—warty. **Versatile**—attached at one point only.

Vertex—the apex. **Verticil**—a whorl.

Vesicle—a small bladder. **Vexillum**—the upper petal of a papilionaceous flower.

Villose—having shaggy hairs. **Viscous**—having a sticky surface.

Vitta—the oil tube in the fruit of the umbellifers.

Warty—covered with hard prominences. **Wavy**—alternately concave and convex.

Wedge-shaped—broad at the end and tapering towards the base.

Wheel-shaped—having a short tube and expanded limb

Whorl—a ring encircling a stem. **Wing**—a membranous appendage.

Wings—the side petals of a papilionaceous plant.

CONTENTS OF THE COLOURED PLATES

And derivations of the Generic Names.

IN this List the plants are numbered in the rotation now generally adopted by field botanists. The book contains a figure of all the genera admitted to be native to our country, including the grasses, ferns, and lycopods.

519

To the scientific and local names the derivation of each generic name has been added, as in the majority of instances that name refers to some characteristic peculiarity of the plant, or the plant's history. In cases where etymologists differ, the derivation given is that most likely to be of use as an aid to memory.

PLATE I

Ranunculaceæ.

1 CLEMATIS VITALBA—Traveller's Joy
    (Greek *clema*, the shoot of a vine, which the branches resemble).
2 THALICTRUM ALPINUM—Alpine Meadow Rue
    (Greek *thallo*, to be green).
3 ANEMONE NEMOROSA—Wind Flower.
    (Greek *anemos*, the wind).
4 ADONIS AUTUMNALIS—Pheasant's Eye
    (the Greek *Adonis*, by whose blood it was stained)
5 MYOSURUS MINIMUS—Mousetail
    (Greek *muos*, a mouse, and *oura*, a tail).
6 RANUNCULUS AQUATILIS—Water Crowfoot
    (Latin *ranunculus*, a small frog).
7 RANUNCULUS FICARIA—Pilewort
8 CALTHA PALUSTRIS—Marsh Marigold
    (Greek *calathos*, a cup, in allusion to the shape).
9 TROLLIUS EUROPÆUS—Globe Flower
    (Old German *troll*, a globe).
10 ERANTHIS HYEMALIS—Winter Aconite
    (Greek *erao*, to love, and *anthos*, a flower, so few blo ...ng with it).
11 HELLEBORUS VIRIDIS—Hellebore
    (Greek *elein*, to injure, and *bora*, food).
12 AQUILEGIA VULGARIS—Columbine
    (Latin *aquila*, an eagle, from the claws of the nectaries)
13 DELPHINIUM AJACIS—Larkspur
    (Latin *delphinus*, a dolphin, from the shape of the upper sepal).
14 ACONITUM NAPELLUS—Monkshood
    (Greek *acon*, a dart, the weapon that was smeared with its poison).
15 ACTÆA SPICATA—Baneberry
    (Greek *akte*, the elder, which it resembles in the leaf).

PLATE VI

PLATE VII

Leguminôsæ.

PLATE VIII

Rosaceæ.

F

PLATE X—(*continued*).

PLATE XI

PLATE XII

PLATE XIII

PLATE XIV

PLATE XVII

PLATE XVIII

PLATE XIX

PLATE XIX—(*continued*).

PLATE XX

PLATE XXI

Lentibulariaceæ.

333 PINGUICULA LUSITANICA—Butterwort
(Latin *pinguis*, fat, from its greasy leaves).

334 UTRICULARIA VULGARIS—Bladderwort
(Latin *utriculus*, a little bladder).

Primulaceæ.

335 PRIMULA VULGARIS—Primrose
(Latin *primus*, first, from its early flowering).

336 CYCLAMEN HEDERIFOLIUM—Sowbread
(Greek *kuklos*, a circle, from its bloom).

337 TRIENTALIS EUROPÆA—Chickweed
(Latin for the third part of a foot, which is the plant's height).

338 HOTTONIA PALUSTRIS—Water Violet
(named after Hotton, the botanist).

339 LYSIMACHIA NUMMULARIA—Loosestrife
(Greek for the English name).

340 ANAGALLIS ARVENSIS—Pimpernel
(Greek, *agallo*, to adorn).

341 CENTUNCULUS MINIMUS—Chaffweed
(the old Latin name).

342 SAMOLUS VALERANDI—Brookweed
(named from the island of Samos, where it is common).

343 GLAUX MARITIMA—Sea Milkwort
(Greek *glaukos*, sea-green).

Plumbaginaceæ.

344 ARMERIA MARITIMA—Thrift
(the Latin name for the Sweet William).

345 STATICE LIMONIUM—Sea Lavender
(Greek for to stop, in allusion to its medicinal properties).

Plantaginaceæ.

346 PLANTAGO LANCEOLATA—Plantain
(Latin *planta*, a plant).

347 LITTORELLA LACUSTRIS—Shoreweed
(so called from its place of growth).

PLATE XXII

Amaranthaceæ.

348 AMARANTHUS BLITUM—Amaranth
(Greek for "unfading").

Chenopodiaceæ.

349 CHENOPODIUM BONUS HENRICUS—Good King Henry
(Greek *chen*, a goose, and *pous*, a foot).

350 OBIONE PORTULACOIDES—Shrubby Sea Purslane
(old Greek name of the plant).

351 ATRIPLEX PATULA—Orache
(Greek *a*, not, and *trephein*, to nourish).

352 BETA MARITIMA—Sea Beet
(Latin *beta*, derived from the Celtic for "food").

353 SALSOLA KALI—Saltwort
(Latin *sal*, salt).

354 SUÆDA MARITIMA—Sea Blite
(Arabic for "a plant yielding soda").

355 SALICORNIA HERBACEA—Glass-wort
(Latin *sal*, salt, and *cornus*, a horn).

Polygonaceæ.

356 POLYGONUM CONVOLVULUS—Climbing Persicaria
(Greek for "many-jointed," in allusion to the stem).

357 RUMEX ACETOSA—Sorrel
(the old Latin name of the sorrel).

358 OXYRIA RENIFORMIS—Mountain Sorrel
(Greek *oxus*, sharp, from its acid flavour).

PLATE   2

PLATE 3

PLATE 4

PLATE 5

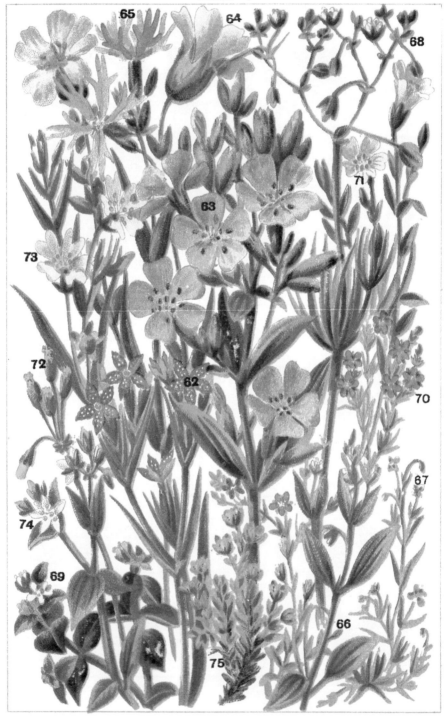

PLATE   6

PLATE 7

PLATE 8

PLATE 9

PLATE 10

PLATE 11

PLATE 12

PLATE 13

PLATE 14

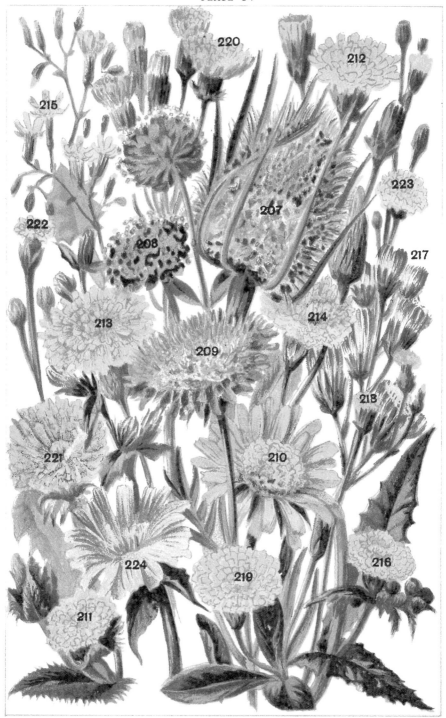

PLATE 15

PLATE 16

PLATE 17

PLATE 18

PLATE 19

PLATE 20

PLATE 21

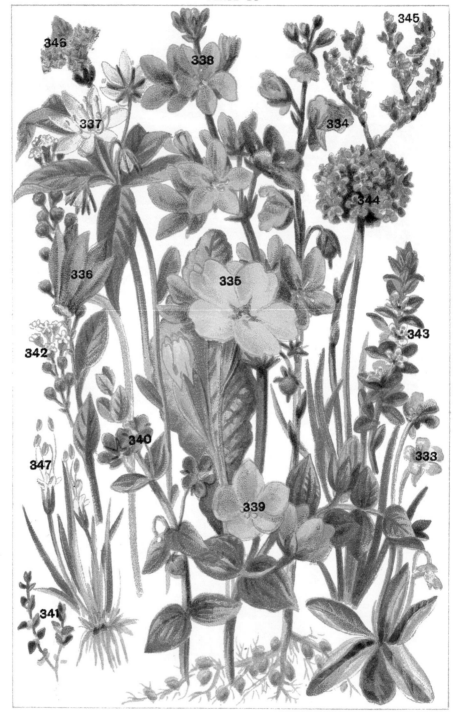

PLATE 22

PLATE 23

PLATE 24

PLATE 25

PLATE 26

PLATE 27

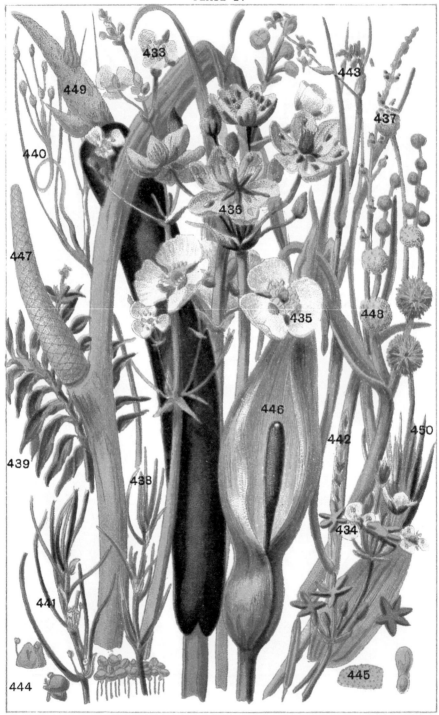

PLATE 28

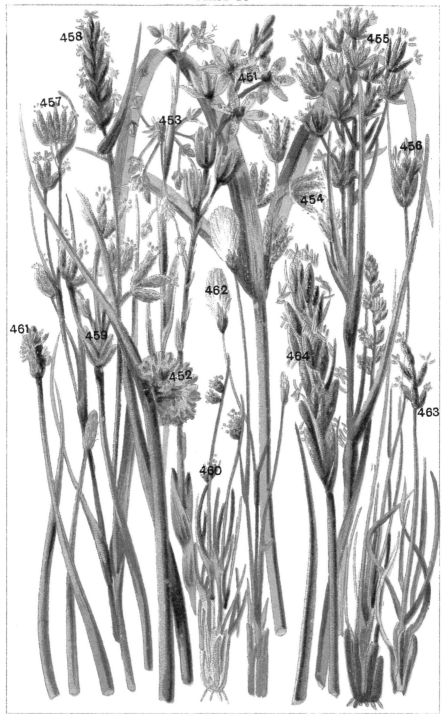

PLATE 29

PLATE 30

PLATE 31

PLATE 32

PLATE 33

PLATE XXIII

PLATE XXIV

Orchidaceæ.

381 GOODYERA REPENS—Goodyera
(named after Goodyer, the botanist).

382 SPIRANTHES ÆSTIVALIS—Lady's Tresses
(Greek for "the spiral flower").

383 NEOTTIA NIDUS AVIS—Bird's Nest
(Greek equivalent of the English name).

384 LISTERA OVATA—Twayblade
(named after Lister, the botanist).

385 EPIPACTIS LATIFOLIA—Helleborine
(Greek name for one of the hellebores).

386 CEPHALANTHERA GRANDIFLORA—White Helleborine
(Greek *kephale*, a head, and *anthos*, a flower).

387 EPIPOGUM GMELINI
(Greek for "beard upwards," from the labellum being turned up).

388 CORALLORHIZA INNATA—Coral Root
(Greek equivalent of the English name).

389 ORCHIS MASCULA—Early Purple Orchis
(Greek name, from the shape of the root).

390 GYMNADENIA CONOPSEA
(Greek for the "naked glands" of the pollinia stalks).

391 HABENARIA CHLORANTHA—Butterfly Orchis
(Latin *habena*, a strap, in allusion to the long spur).

392 ACERAS ANTHROPOPHORA—Man Orchis
(Greek *a* without, and *keras*, a horn, from the absence of the spur).

393 NEOTINEA INTACTA
(Greek *neo*, new, and *tinea*, the old name of the plant which was changed as being
that of a genus of moths).

394 HERMINIUM MONORCHIS—Musk Orchis
(from the Greek for the foot of a bed-post, in allusion to the shape of the root).

395 OPHRYS APIFERA—Bee Orchis
(Greek *ophrus*, the eyebrow, which the plant was used to blacken).

396 MALAXIS PALUDOSA—Bog Orchis
(Greek for "softening," in allusion to the tender growth).

397 LIPARIS LOESELII
(Greek *liparos*, fatty, from the leaves).

398 CYPRIPEDIUM CALCEOLUS—Lady's Slipper
(Greek *Kupris*, Venus, and *podion*, a slipper).

PLATE XXV

Coniferæ.

399 PINUS SYLVESTRIS—Scotch Fir
(Celtic *pin*, a mountain top).

400 JUNIPERUS COMMUNIS—Juniper
(the old Latin name).

401 TAXUS BACCATA—Yew
(Greek *toxos*, a bow).

Iridaceæ.

402 IRIS FŒTIDISSIMA—Gladdon
(Greek for "the rainbow").

403 GLADIOLUS COMMUNIS—Gladiolus
(Latin *gladius*, a sword, from the shape of the leaves).

404 SISYRINCHIUM ANCEPS
(Greek for "the snout of a pig").

405 TRICHONEMA COLUMNÆ
(Greek *trichos*, a hair, and *nema*, a filament).

406 CROCUS VERNUS—Crocus
(Greek *kroke*, a thread, from the dried stigmas sold as saffron).

Amaryllidaceæ.

407 NARCISSUS PSEUDO-NARCISSUS—Daffodil
(Greek *narke*, stupor, from the effect of the smell of the bloom)

PLATE XXV—(*continued*).

408 GALANTHUS NIVALIS—Snowdrop
(Greek for "the milk-white flower").

409 LEUCOJUM ÆSTIVUM—Snowflake
(Greek *leukos*, white, and *ion*, a violet).

Liliaceæ.

410 LILIUM MARTAGON—Purple Lily
(Celtic *li*, whiteness).

411 TULIPA SYLVESTRIS—Tulip
(Persian *tolibun*, a turban).

412 FRITILLARIA MELEAGRIS—Fritillary
(Latin *fritillus*, a dice box).

413 ALLIUM URSINUM—Ramsons
(Celtic *all*, pungent).

414 GAGEA LUTEA
(named after Gage, the botanist).

415 ORNITHOGALUM PYRENAICUM—Star of Bethlehem
(Greek for "bird's milk," probably the "dove's dung" of Samaria).

PLATE XXVI

416 SCILLA VERNA—Squill
(Arabic *asgyl*, the name of the plant).

417 HYACINTHUS NONSCRIPTUS—Blue Bell
(the name of the boy from whose blood Apollo made the flower).

418 MUSCARI RACEMOSUM—Grape Hyacinth
(named from its musk-like fragrance).

419 LLOYDIA SEROTINA
(named after Llhwyd, who first found it in Britain)

420 SIMETHIS BICOLOR
(named after the Sicilian nymph).

421 ASPARAGUS OFFICINALIS—Asparagus
(the old Greek name, meaning "the tearer," from the spikes with which some of the species are armed).

422 RUSCUS ACULEATUS—Butcher's Broom
(formerly bruscus, from the Celtic *bruskelen*, the box-holly).

423 MAIANTHEMUM BIFOLIUM—May Lily
(Latin equivalent of the English name).

424 CONVALLARIA MAJALIS—Lily of the Valley
(Latin *convallis*, a valley).

425 POLYGONATUM MULTIFLORUM—Solomon's Seal
(Greek for "many knees," in allusion to the stem).

Trilliaceæ.

426 PARIS QUADRIFOLIA—Herb Paris
(Latin *par*, equal, on account of its equal leaves).

Dioscoreaceæ.

427 TAMUS COMMUNIS—Black Bryony
(the old Latin name).

Melanthaceæ.

428 COLCHICUM AUTUMNALE—Meadow Saffron
(from Colchis, where it grew abundantly).

429 TOFIELDIA PALUSTRIS—Scotch Asphodel
(named after Tofield, the botanist).

Hydrocharidaceæ.

430 HYDROCHARIS MORSUS-RANÆ—Frogbit
(Greek *hudor*, water, and *charis*, elegance).

431 ELODEA CANADENSIS—Water Thyme
(Greek *elodes*, growing in a marsh).

432 STRATIOTES ALOIDES—Water Soldier
(Greek for "a soldier").

PLATE XXVII

Alismaceæ.

433 ALISMA PLANTAGO—Water Plantain
(Celtic *alis*, water).

434 ACTINOCARPUS DAMASONIUM—Star Fruit
(equivalent of the English name).

435 SAGITTARIA SAGITTIFOLIA—Arrow Head
(Latin *sagitta*, an arrow, the shape of the leaves).

436 BUTOMUS UMBELLATUS—Flowering Rush
(Greek *bous*, an ox, and *temno*, to cut, from the effect of the leaves on the mouths of cattle).

437 TRIGLOCHIN PALUSTRE—Marsh Arrowgrass
(Greek for "three points," being those of the capsules).

438 SCHEUCHZERIA PALUSTRIS
(named after the Scheuchzers, who were Swiss botanists).

Naiadaceæ.

439 POTAMOGETON DENSUS—Pond Weed
(Greek *potamos*, a river, and *geiton*, a neighbour).

440 RUPPIA MARITIMA—Tassel Pond Weed
(named after Ruppius, a botanist).

441 ZANNICHELLIA PALUSTRIS—Horned Pond Weed
(named after Zannichelli, a botanist).

442 ZOSTERA MARINA—Grass Wrack
(Greek *zoster*, a riband, from the leaves).

443 NAIAS FLEXILIS
(Latin for "a water nymph").

Lemnaceæ.

444 LEMNA MINOR—Duckweed
(Greek *lemna*, derived from *lepis*, a scale).

445 WOLFFIA ARRHIZA
(named after Wolff, the botanist).

Araceæ.

446 ARUM MACULATUM—Lords and Ladies
(Greek *aron*, the same plant).

447 ACORUS CALAMUS—Sweet Flag
(Greek *a*, out ; and *kore*, the pupil of the eye, from the use of the plant in medicine).

Typhaceæ.

448 SPARGANIUM RAMOSUM—Bur Reed
(Greek *sparganon*, a little band, like its leaves).

449 TYPHA LATIFOLIA—Bulrush
(Greek *tuphos*, a marsh).

Restiaceæ.

450 ERIOCAULON SEPTANGULARE—Pipe Wort
(Greek *erion*, wool ; and *kaulos*, the stem).

PLATE XXVIII

Juncaceæ.

451 NARTHÉCIUM OSSIFRAGUM—Bog Asphodel
(Greek *narthes*, a rod).

452 JUNCUS COMMUNIS—Rush
(Latin *jungo*, to join, from the stems being used as wrappings).

453 LUZULA PILOSA—Hairy Wood Rush
(Italian *luzziola*, a glowworm, from the flowers glittering with dew in the moonlight).

Cyperaceæ.

454 CYPERUS LONGUS—Sweet Cyperus
(Greek *kuprios*, copper, from the colour of the flowers).

455 CLADIUM MARISCUS—Twig-rush
(Greek *kladios*, a branch, from its many flowering branches).

456 SCHŒNUS NIGRICANS—Bog Rush
(Greek *schoinos*, a cord, from the stem being made into ropes).

457 RHYNCOSPORA ALBA—Beak Rush
(Greek for "beaked seed").

PLATE XXVIII—(*continued*).

458 BLYSMUS COMPRESSUS
(Greek *blusmos*, a spring, from the plant's habitat).

459 SCIRPUS LACUSTRIS—Club Rush
(old Latin name for "the rush without a knot").

460 ISOLEPIS SETACEA—Mud Rush
(Greek for "equal scales," in allusion to the inflorescence).

461 ELEOCHARIS PALUSTRIS—Spike Rush
(Greek for "the delight of the marsh").

462 ERIOPHORUM ALPINUM—Cotton Grass
(Greek *erion*, wool, and *phero*, to bear).

463 KOBRESIA CARICINA
(named after Kobres, "a patron of botany").

464 CAREX PANICULATA—Sedge
(Greek *keiro*, to cut—with the angled stems).

PLATE XXIX

Gramineæ.

465 LEERSIA ORYZOIDES—Cut Grass
(named after Leers, the botanist).

466 SPARTINA STRICTA—Cord Grass
(Greek *spartine*, a rope).

467 CYNODON DACTYLON—Dog's Tooth Grass
(Greek equivalent of English name).

468 DIGITARIA HUMIFUSA—Finger Grass
(Latin *digitus*, a finger).

PANICUM CRUSGALLI—Panic Grass
(Latin *panis*, bread, the seeds having formerly been used for flour).

469 SETARIA VIRIDIS—Bristle Grass
(Latin *seta*, a bristle).

470 PHALARIS ARUNDINACEA—Canary Grass
(Greek *phalos*, shining, from the seeds).

471 ANTHOXANTHUM ODORATUM—Vernal Grass
(Greek, "the yellow flower," from the colour of the bloom).

472 HIEROCHLOE BOREALIS—Holy Grass
(Greek for "the sacred grass," owing to its dedication to the Virgin and its use for strewing in churches).

473 PHLEUM PRATENSE—Cat's Tail Grass
(Greek *phleos*, old name of the bulrush, which the plant somewhat resembles),

474 ALOPECURUS PRATENSIS—Fox-tail Grass
(Greek equivalent of English name).

475 KNAPPIA AGROSTIDEA
(named after Knapp, the botanist).

GASTRIDIUM LENDIGERUM
(Greek *gastridion*, the little swelling, which is seen at the base of the spikelet).

476 POLYPOGON LITTORALIS—Beard Grass
(Greek for "many-bearded").

PLATE XXX

477 MILIUM EFFUSUM—Millet Grass
(Latin *millia*, thousands, from the seeds).

APERA SPICA VENTI—Bent Grass
(Latin *aperio*, to open).

478 AGROSTIS CANINA—Bent Grass
(Greek *agros*, a field).

479 AMMOPHILA ARUNDINACEA—Marram
(Greek, "a lover of sand," from its habitat).

480 ARUNDO PHRAGMITES—Reed
(the old Latin name).

481 CALAMAGROSTIS LANCEOLATA—Small Reed
(Greek for "the field reed").

PLATE XXX—(*continued*).

482 SESLERIA CŒRULEA—Moor Grass
(named after Sesler, a botanist).

483 AIRA FLEXUOSA—Hair Grass
(the Greek name of Lolium, facetiously misapplied).
LAGURUS OVATUS—Hare's Tail Grass
(Greek equivalent of English name).

484 AVENA PRATENSIS—Oat Grass
(the old Latin name).

485 ARRHENATHERUM AVENACEUM—False Oat Grass
(Greek *arrhen*, a male, and *ather*, an awn).

486 HOLCUS LANATUS—Soft Grass
(the old Latin name, said to mean "hardy on a wall").

487 TRIODIA DECUMBENS—Heath Grass
(Greek *treis*, three, and *odous*, a tooth).

488 KOELERIA CRISTATA
(named after Koeler, the botanist).

PLATE XXXI

489 MELICA UNIFLORA—Melic Grass
(Latin *mel*, honey, from the flavour of the stem).

490 MOLINIA CŒRULEA—Purple Melic
(named after a Chilian botanist).

491 CATABROSA AQUATICA—Whorl Grass
(Greek *catabrosis*, a gnawing, from the bitten end of the glumes)

492 GLYCERIA AQUATICA—Meadow Grass
(Greek *glykeros*, sweet).
SCHLEROCHLOA MARITIMA—Meadow Grass
(Greek for "hard grass").

493 POA PRATENSIS—Meadow Grass
(Greek *pra*, a pasturage).

494 BRIZA MEDIA—Quaking Grass
(Greek *britho*, to droop).

495 CYNOSURUS CRISTATUS—Dog's Tail Grass
(Greek equivalent of English name).

496 DACTYLIS GLOMERATA—Cock's Foot
(Greek *daktulos*, a finger).

497 FESTUCA OVINA—Fescue Grass
(Latin *festuca*, the shoot of a tree).

498 BROMUS ERECTUS—Brome Grass
(Greek *broma*, food).

499 BRACHYPODIUM SYLVATICUM—False Brome
(Greek "short-footed," from the spikelet).

PLATE XXXII

500 TRITICUM CANINUM—Bearded Wheat
(Latin *tritum*, ground—into flour).

501 LOLIUM PERENNE—Rye Grass
(old Latin name).

502 ELYMUS ARENARIUS—Lyme Grass
(from Elyma, the Greek town, where the plant is common).

503 HORDEUM PRATENSE—Barley
(the old Latin name).

504 NARDUS STRICTA—Mat Grass
(Greek *nardos*, a sweet-smelling substance).

505 LEPTURUS FILIFORMIS—Hard Grass
(Greek *leptos*, slender, and *oura*, a tail).

Lycopodiaceæ.

526 LYCOPODIUM CLAVATUM—Club Moss.
(Greek, " a wolf's foot," in allusion to the branches).

527 SELAGINELLA SELAGINOIDES—Selaginella
(diminutive of *selago*, the Latin for the hedge-hyssop).

528 ISOETES LACUSTRIS—Quillwort
(Greek *isos*, alike, *etos*, the year, that is, "evergreen ").

Marsileaceæ.

529 PILULARIA GLOBULIFERA—Pillwort
(Latin *pilula*, a little pill).

Equisetaceæ.

530 EQUISETUM UMBROSUM—Horse Tail
(Latin *equus*, a horse, and *seta*, a bristle).

PLATE XXXIII

Filices.

506 PSEUDATHYRIUM ALPESTRE
(Greek "the false athyrium" for which see below).

507 SCOLOPENDRIUM VULGARE—Hart's Tongue
(from *scolopendra*, the centipede).

508 BLECHNUM BOREALE—Hard Fern
(Greek *blechnon*, a fern).

509 OPHIOGLOSSUM VULGATUM—Adder's Tongue
(Greek Equivalent of English name).

~~~~~~~~

LIST OF FERNS

(used as embellishments on the pages indicated).

510 CETERACH OFFICINARUM—Scale Fern, p. 132.
(Arabic *chetherak*).

511 GYMNOGRAMMA LEPTOPHYLLA—Gymnogram, p. 82.
(Greek " naked writing," from the sori).

512 WOODSIA HYPERBOREA—Woodsia, p. 46.
(named after Woods, the botanist).

513 POLYPODIUM VULGARE—Polypody, p. 30.
(Greek " many footed," from the segments of the fronds).

514 ALLOSORUS CRISPUS—Parsley Fern, p. 89.
(Greek *allos*, various, and *sorus*).

515 CYSTOPTERIS FRAGILIS—Bladder Fern, p. 15.
(Greek *kustis*, a bladder, and *pteris*, a fern).

516 POLYSTICHUM LONCHITIS—Holly Fern, p. 55.
(Greek *polus*, many, and *stichos*, a row).

517 LASTRÆA FILIX-MAS—Male Fern, p. 45.
(named after De Lastre, the botanist).

518 ATHYRIUM FILIX-FŒMINA—Lady Fern, p. 54.
(Greek *a*, not, and *thureos*, a shield, it not having a shield-like indusium).

519 ASPLENIUM ADIANTUM NIGRUM—Black Spleenwort, p. 61.
(Greek *a*, not, and *splen*, spleen, from the medicinal properties).

520 PTERIS AQUILINA—The Brake, p. 88.
(Greek for " a fern").

521 ADIANTUM CAPILLUS VENERIS—Maidenhair, p. 16.
(Greek *adiantos*, dry, from its habitat).

522 TRICHOMANES RADICANS—Bristle Fern, p. 1.
(the old Greek name).

523 HYMENOPHYLLUM TUNBRIDGENSE—Filmy Fern, p. 35.
(Greek "a membranous leaf").

524 OSMUNDA REGALIS—Royal Fern, p. 133.
(named from Osmund, who hid his wife and child under its fronds).

525 BOTRYCHIUM LUNARIA—Moonwort, p. 31.
(Greek *botrus*, a bunch of grapes, from the branched clusters of capsules).

THE ORDERS,

I N this list the particulars given are such as are generally sufficient to distinguish the orders as found in Britain from each other, and no more, the object being to make the descriptions as brief as possible. The next index shows how. the genera of each order are distinguishable, and the third index is devoted to the distinctions between species and species. In some orders there is but one genus ; in some cases that genus has but one species, and then the diagrams in the next index will enable the student to identify the flowers at once. In all cases the diagrams should be referred to.

Aceraceæ,　Plate vi.
trees—leaves simple, generally lobed, opposite, and without stipules ; flowers green and small ; sepals four to nine ; petals four to nine, imbricate in bud ; stamens five to twelve on a disk, hypogynous ; carpels two ; fruit a samara.

Alismaceæ,　Plate xxvii.
water plants—leaves broad, net veined, and radical ; monocotyledon ; perianth six ; stamens six ; ovary superior and free from perianth ; fruit of many carpels.

Amaranthaceæ,　Plate xxii.
weedy herbs—stems not jointed ; leaves without stipules ; perianth three to five leaved, often with bracts ; flowers unisexual; stamens three to five, hypogynous, and opposite the perianth segments ; anthers often unilocular ; ovary superior, single or double celled ; styles one or wanting ; fruit indehiscent.

Amaryllidaceæ,　Plate xxv.
herbs—bulbous and scape-bearing ; leaves flat, fleshy, indistinctly nerved, and all radical ; flowers large and generally bright; monocotyledon ; perianth six-parted ; stamens six, inserted at the bottom of the perianth segments ; anthers opening inwards ; ovary inferior and adnate with the perianth tube.

Apocynaceæ,　Plate xvii.
shrubs—often with milky juice ; leaves entire, opposite and without stipules ; flowers purple and pentagonal ; calyx in five ; corolla in five, twisted in bud ; stamens five, on the corolla ; stigma shaped like an hour-glass ; fruit two follicles.

Aquifoliaceæ,　Plate xvii.
evergreen trees or shrubs—leaves simple, prickly, and without stipules ; flowers axillary ; calyx in four or six, lobes imbricated ; corolla four or six, imbricate in bud ; stamens four or six, on the corolla, and alternate with the lobes ; ovary superior ; fruit a fleshy berry.

Araceæ,　Plate xxvii.
herbs—leaves sheathing at the base, convolute in æstivation, and often with branching veins ; flowers on a spadix, enclosed in a leafy sheath ; monocotyledon ; perianth wanting ; stamens indefinite ; seeds pulpy.

Araliaceæ,　Plate xi.
climbing shrubs or low herbs—with alternate lobed leaves and green flowers ; calyx three or five cleft, half inferior ; petals five or ten, occasionally wanting ; stamens as many or twice as many as the petals, from the margin of an epigynous disk ; ovary inferior, with two or more cells ; styles as many as the cells ; fruit fleshy or dry, of several single-seeded cells.

Aristolochiaceæ,　Plate xxii.
climbing shrubs or low herbs—leaves alternate ; wood without concentric zones ; perianth in three, tubular, often with a dilated limb, free and adnate with ovary ; stamens six to twelve, epigynous ; ovary inferior, three to six-celled, with numerous valves ; style simple ; stigma rayed ; fruit a six-locular capsule or berry.

Balsaminaceæ,　Plate vi.
succulent herbs—leaves without stipules, simple and alternate ; flowers axillary and yellow ; sepals, five, irregular, deciduous, imbricate in æstivation, one of them

BALSAMINACEÆ, Plate vi. (cont.).

spurred; petals four, irregular, united in pairs; stamens five, hypogynous, filaments more or less united at the end; capsule bursting with elastic valves.

Berberidaceæ, Plate i.

spiny shrubs—the spines being in threes; leaves alternate, compound, exstipulate, and ciliated on the serratures; flowers pendulous; sepals three, four, or six, in a double row, bracteated and deciduous; petals three, four, or six, free, glandular at the base; stamens three, four, or six, hypogynous.

Betulaceæ, Plate xxiii.

trees or shrubs—leaves alternate and simple, often with the ribs running straight from the mid-rib to the margin; flowers in catkins; perianth in four or none; stamens four, opposite each division of the perianth; filaments very short and distinct; style none; stigmas two, thread-like; fruit small, double-seeded, inde-hiscent, and not enclosed in a cup.

Boraginaceæ, Plate xx.

herbs—with rough alternate leaves and flowers in spikes; calyx in five; corolla in five, regular, imbricate in bud; stamens five, on the corolla, and alternate with its segments; carpels united into a superior four-lobed ovary; fruit of four nutlets.

Campanulaceæ, Plate xiii.

herbs—leaves entire, alternate, and without stipules; calyx in five, lobes persistent; corolla in five; stamens five, on the ovary; filaments broad and valvate at the base; ovary inferior, two to eight-celled; style thick and hairy.

Caprifoliaceæ, Plate xiii.

shrubs or herbs—leaves opposite, and gener-ally without stipules; calyx in four or five, attached to the ovary and having bracts: corolla monopetalous, four or five-cleft; stamens four or five, on the corolla, and alternate with its lobes; ovary in-ferior, three, four, or five-celled; fruit not a drupe.

Caryophyllaceæ, Plate v.

herbs—mostly with stems tumid at the joints; leaves entire and opposite; flowers regular, and white or red; sepals four or five, distinct or connected in a tube; petals four or five, clawed; stamens as many as, or double the number of petals, hypogynous; anthers opening longi-tudinally; capsule opening at the top with teeth.

Celastraceæ, Plate vi.

shrubs or trees—leaves simple and mostly opposite; flowers in axillary cymes; calyx four or five-cleft, imbricate in æstivation; petals four or five, inserted into the margin of a hypogynous fleshy disk; stamens four or five, alternate with the petals, perigynous; seed with bright orange-coloured arillus.

Chenopodiaceæ, Plate xxii.

weedy herbs—with jointed stems; leaves generally alternate and without stipules; flowers small and inconspicuous; perianth five, imbricate in the bud, free, deeply cleft, generally without bracts; flowers often unisexual; stamens one, two, or five, generally five, rising from the base of the perianth and opposite the segments; anthers two-celled; ovary superior; style divided, rarely simple; fruit indehiscent, enclosed in the perianth, which often be-comes fleshy.

Cistaceæ, Plate iv.

herbaceous plants or shrubs—with entire leaves; flowers regular; sepals five, two smaller than the rest, and three twisted in æstivation; petals five, crumpled and twisted in æstivation the contrary way to the sepals; stamens many, free, and hypogynous; ovary tripartite and single-celled.

Compositæ, Plates xiv., xv., xvi.

herbs or shrubs—flowers in a dense head on a common receptacle, surrounded by an involucre; calyx wanting, or with a mem-branous or pappose limb; corolla funnel-shaped, ligulate or bilabiate, or wanting; stamens five on the corolla; anthers united into a tube round the style; ovary inferior, with one erect ovule.

Coniferæ, Plate xxv.

trees or shrubs—leaves linear, rigid, and evergreen, with parallel veins; male flowers in a catkin, female flowers in a cone; ovary in the cones like a scale; ovules naked.

Convolvulaceæ, Plate xviii.

herbs—generally twining, leaves or scales alternate; calyx of five sepals imbricate in two rows: corolla in four or five with the limb plaited; stamens four or five on the corolla; carpels united into a superior two or three-celled, few seeded, pistil, with erect ovules; embryo curved; cotyledons plaited.

Cornaceæ, Plate xi.

herbs or trees—leaves ovate and opposite; flowers small, growing in heads or umbels; calyx in four or five, attached to the ovary; petals four or five, broad at the base; sta-mens four or five, inserted with the petals; ovary inferior; style filiform; stigma simple; fruit a drupe with a two-celled nut.

Crassulaceæ, Plate x.

succulent herbs—leaves thick and fleshy, and without stipules; flowers symmetrical; sepals three to twenty, united at the base; petals three to twenty, inserted at the base of the calyx; stamens three to twenty, or twice as many as petals: perigynous; car-pels three to twenty, superior, opposite the petals, and many-seeded.

Cruciferæ, Plates ii., iii.

herbs with not unwholesome pungent watery juice—leaves alternate, and without sti-pules; flowers regular, beginning in corymbs and becoming racemose; sepals four, deciduous; petals four, stalked, cru-ciform; stamens six, four longer than the rest, hypogynous; fruit a pouch or pod.

Cucurbitaceæ, Plate ix.

succulent climbing plants—leaves with ten-drils in the place of stipules ; flowers in axillary racemes ; calyx five-cleft, the tube adnate with the ovary ; petals five, often with reticulated veins ; stamens five, more or less cohering ; seeds flat, in an arillus.

Cupuliferæ, Plate xxiii.

trees or shrubs—leaves alternate, simple, often, with veins straight from mid-rib to margin ; flowers in catkins ; fruit in a cup ; perianth five or six-lobed ; stamens five to twenty, inserted into the base of scales, or of a membranous perianth.

Cyperaceæ, Plate xxviii.

the sedges—leaves with entire sheaths, solid stems, often angular, and frequently with-out joints ; monocotyledon ; flowers glu-maceous ; stamens one to twelve, definite, and hypogynous.

Dioscoreaceæ, Plate xxvi.

climbing plants — leaves broad, netted-veined, alternate, and stalked ; flowers in racemes, and small and bracteated ; mono-cotyledon ; perianth six-parted ; stamens six, from the base of the perianth ; stamens and pistils in separate flowers ; style deeply trifid ; ovary inferior and adnate with the perianth tube.

Dipsaceæ, Plate xiv.

herbs—leaves opposite or whorled ; flowers in heads ; calyx in four, enclosed in an involucel ; corolla four, with the limb oblique ; stamens four, on the corolla ; anthers free ; carpel solitary, inferior, with one pendulous ovule.

Droseraceæ, Plate iv.

marsh herbs—radical leaves with glandular capitate hair s ; flowers regular ; sepals five, imbricat eand persistent ; petals five ; stamens five or ten, free, and hypogynous ; ovary single-celled.

Elatinaceæ, Plate iv.

small marsh herbs—leaves in a whorl, spathu-late, and with stipules ; flowers small and axillary ; sepals three to five ; petals three to five, sessile ; stamens three to five, or six to ten, free, and hypogynous.

Eleagnaceæ, Plate xxii.

shrubs with silvery scales — leaves entire, alternate, and without stipules ; male flowers in catkins ; perianth of male flower in three or four ; stamens four to eight, inserted on the throat ; ovary superior ; fruit crustaceous.

Empetraceæ, Plate xxii.

low shrubby evergreens — heath-like in aspect ; leaves alternate ; stamens and pistils in separate flowers and on different plants ; flowers inconspicuous ; no calyx ; no corolla ; perianth of four to six hypogynous scales in two rows ; stamens two or three, alternate with the inner row of scales ; ovary free on a fleshy disk.

Equisetaceæ, Plate xxxii.

herbaceous plants—with jointed, furrowed hollow stems and whorls of scale-like leaves at the joints ; spores on metamor-phosed leaf-bearing stems ; acotyledon.

Ericaceæ, Plate xvii.

low shrubs—leaves mostly rigid, evergreen, and without stipules ; calyx in four or five ; corolla in four or five ; stamens eight or ten, free from corolla ; ovary in a disk, with four or more cells.

Euphorbiaceæ, Plate xxiii.

herbs—with milky stems ; leaves entire ; anthers and pistils in different flowers and on different plants ; flowers often in an involucre ; perianth three or four-lobed or wanting ; stamens one, or more than eight ; capsules bursting elastically.

Filices, Plate xxxiii.

leafy plants—of varied structure, fructifica-tion consisting of seeds or sporules in-cluded in capsules ; thecæ or sporangia either naked or covered with a membrane, and generally collected into clusters on the edge or under side of the leaves ; acotyle-don.

Frankeniaceæ, Plate iv.

low-branched herb—leaves opposite, without stipules, but with a membranous sheathing base ; flowers red, small, and axillary ; sepals four, five, or six, combined into a furrowed tube ; petals four, five, or six, clawed ; stamens four, five, or six, free, hypogynous, alternating with petals ; ovary single-celled, with two or four valves.

Fumariaceæ, Plate ii.

slender herbs—with brittle stems and watery juice ; leaves alternate, divided and exstipu-late ; flowers irregular and in racemes ; sepals two, deciduous ; petals four, parallel, one or two swollen at the base ; stamens six, in two bundles, opposite to the outer petals, hypogynous ; ovary single-celled, with two opposite parietal placentas.

Gentianaceæ, Plate xvii.

smooth herbs—leaves entire, sessile, ribbed, generally opposite, and without stipules ; calyx four to ten-lobed ; corolla four to ten-lobed ; stamens on the corolla, and alternate with its lobes ; ovary superior, single or double celled ; fruit a capsule or berry.

Geraniaceæ, Plate vi.

herbs — with swollen stem joints ; leaves lobed and stipuled, opposite or alternate, and then opposite the peduncles ; sepals five, imbricated in æstivation ; petals, five-clawed, and twisted in æstivation ; stamens twice as many as petals ; carpels five, elastic, combined into a pistil with five cells and a long beak.

Gramineæ, Plates xxix., xxx., xxxi., xxxii.

the grasses — leaves with split sheaths; hollow stems, jointed, sometimes branched; monocotyledon; flowers glumaceous; stamens hypogynous, one to six, but usually three.

Grossulariaceæ, Plate x.

shrubs—often spiny; leaves rough, lobed and alternate; flowers small and greenish; calyx four or five-cleft, growing from top of ovary; petals four or five at the mouth of the calyx tube; stamens four or five, alternate with petals, perigynous; ovary inferior; fruit a pulpy berry.

Haloragaceæ, Plate ix.

aquatic herbs—leaves often whorled; flowers very small; calyx in three or four parts, adnate with ovary; petals generally wanting; stamens one, two, four, or eight, perigynous; ovary inferior and one to four-celled; seeds solitary, pendulous and perispermic.

Hydrocharidaceæ, Plate xxvi.

water plants—leaves floating or submerged, radical, and with serrated margins; conspicuous flowers; monocotyledon; flowers unisexual, perfect or imperfect, with a spathe; perianth in six segments, three herbaceous and three petaloid, the latter occasionally wanting; stamens three or six; free from style; ovary inferior and adnate to perianth.

Hypericaceæ, Plate vi.

herbs or shrubs—leaves mostly opposite, without stipules, and marked with pellucid dots; flowers yellow; sepals four or five, persistent, imbricate, and often dotted; petals four or five twisted in æstivation, and often dotted; stamens hypogynous, many, and united into three or five bundles; capsule three, four, or five-celled.

Illecebraceæ, Plate x.

branching herbs—leaves entire and sessile; flowers small; sepals four or five; petals four or five, or wanting; stamens five or less, perigynous; ovary superior.

Iridaceæ, Plate xxv.

herbs—leaves usually equitant and in two ranks; flowers spathaceous and handsome; monocotyledon; perianth six-parted, convolute in the bud in two circles: stamens three, superposed to the outer segments of the perianth; style one; stigmas three, often petaloid; ovary inferior and adnate with the tube of the perianth.

Juncaceæ, Plate xxviii.

the rushes—leaves parallel-veined, narrow, small, and round—occasionally wanting; flowers small, brown, and scarious; monocotyledon; perianth six-parted; stamens six or three; stigmas three, sometimes one.

Labiatæ, Plate xix.

herbs with square stems—leaves generally opposite and aromatic; flowers irregular and in whorls or cymes; calyx tubular, bilabiate, or in five; corolla monopetalous,

Labiatæ, Plate xix. (*cont.*).

hypogynous, and generally bilabiate; stamens on the corolla, two or four, half-longer than the rest; carpels united into a superior four-celled ovary, with the style rising between the lobes.

Leguminosæ, Plate vii.

herbs or shrubs—leaves mostly ternate or pinnate, alternate and stipuled, with or without tendrils; flowers papilionaceous: calyx four or five-cleft: petals five, irregular, springing from the bottom of the calyx; stamens 10, perigynous; carpel solitary, superior, ripening into a legume.

Lemnaceæ, Plate xxvii.

small, stemless, free, floating plants, with cellular netted-veined leaves, and axillary flowers; monocotyledon; perianth wanting; stamens one or two.

Lentibulariaceæ, Plate xxi.

small marsh herbs — leaves radical and undivided, or compound and bearing bladders; calyx in four or five; corolla in four or five, or two-lipped with a spur; stamens two on the corolla; ovary single-celled and superior; fruit a many-seeded capsule.

Liliaceæ, Plate xxv.

herbs — leaves parallel-veined, narrow, sheathing, and never articulated with the stem; flowers generally large; monocotyledon; perianth of six parts, in two circles; stamens six; anthers opening inwards; fruit loculicidal; ovary superior and free from the perianth.

Linaceæ, Plate vi.

herbs—leaves entire and without stipules; sepals four or five, persistent, imbricated in æstivation; petals four or five, fugacious, twisted in æstivation, and clawed; stamens four or five, hypogynous, alternate with petals, with small teeth between them; capsule three, four, or five-celled.

Loranthaceæ, Plate xiii.

parasitical shrubs—leaves entire, opposite, fleshy, and without stipules; calyx adnate with the inferior ovary; petals four; stamens four, epiphyllous; stamens and pistils often in different plants; fruit a pulpy berry.

Lycopodiaceæ, Plate xxxii.

leafy plants; fructification sessile in the axils of leaves or in the bracts of a cone; acotyledon.

Lythraceæ, Plate ix.

herbs—leaves usually opposite, entire, and without stipules; flowers regular; calyx cleft in three, often with intermediate teeth; petals three or six, crumpled in æstivation; stamens six or twelve, perigynous; ovary superior.

Malvaceæ, Plate vi.

herbs, shrubs, or trees — leaves alternate with stipules, and generally covered with soft down; flowers regular and axillary; sepals five, valvate in æstivation; petals five, twisted in æstivation; stamens many, united into a tube adherent to the claws of the petals; ovary many-celled.

Marsileaceæ,　　Plate xxxii.

plants — rooting in moist earth ; slender circinate leaves ; sori bisexual ; spores in globular masses invested by hardened mucilage ; acotyledon.

Melanthaceæ,　　Plate xxvi.

herbs — occasionally with bulbous roots ; leaves linear, sheathing at the base, and with parallel nerves ; monocotyledon ; perianth in six parts, or tubular by cohesion of the segment claws ; stamens six ; anthers extrorse ; fruit septicidal ; ovary superior, and free from perianth.

Myricaceæ,　　Plate xxiii.

aromatic shrubs — leaves alternate ; flowers in catkins, small and green ; no perianth ; stamens two to eight ; anthers two or four-celled, opening longitudinally ; ovary free and single-celled ; fruit drupaceous.

Naiadaceæ,　　Plate xxvii.

immersed aquatic plants — with jointed stems and parallel-veined leaves, sheathing stipules ; flowers inconspicuous ; monocotyledon ; perianth of three or four scales, or wanting ; stamens four ; ovary superior ; fruit of one to four carpels.

Nymphæaceæ,　　Plate i.

aquatic herbs — with cordate or peltate floating leaves, and showy solitary flowers ; sepals four, five, or six, partially petaloid, passing into numerous petals, and stamens imbricated in several rows, and placed on a fleshy disk surrounding a many-celled and many seeded ovary.

Oleaceæ,　　Plate xvii.

trees or shrubs — leaves simple or compound, opposite, and without stipules ; calyx in four, sometimes wanting ; corolla in four, valvate in bud, sometimes wanting ; stamens two on the corolla ; ovary without hypogynous disk ; fruit a berry or key.

Onagraceæ,　　Plate ix.

herbs or shrubs — leaves entire, and frequently opposite and not dotted ; flowers regular and showy ; calyx in two or four, tubular, adnate with ovary, and valvate in æstivation ; petals two or four, twisted in æstivation ; stamens two, four, or eight, perigynous ; ovary inferior, one to four-celled, many-seeded ; fruit a berry or capsule.

Orchidaceæ,　　Plate xxiv.

herbaceous plants, with knob-like roots — flowers usually handsome, in spikes or racemes ; monocotyledon ; perianth of six segments, in two rows, and irregular in shape ; stamens three, two of which are generally abortive, so that, with one exception, the British genera have but one perfect anther ; stamens and style united ; ovary one-celled, inferior, and adnate with the tube of the perianth.

Orobanchaceæ,　　Plate xix.

leafless root parasites, with brownish flowers — calyx in four or five ; corolla in four or five gaping ; stamens four, two long and two short ; ovary one-celled.

Oxalidaceæ,　　Plate vi.

small herbs — leaves mostly trifoliate, acrid, and sensitive ; flowers axillary ; sepals five, imbricate in æstivation ; petals five, often coherent at the base, twisted in æstivation ; stamens ten, five opposite the petals and longer than the rest ; hypogynous ; carpels united into a pistil, with five polyspermous cells ; fruit bursting elastically.

Papaveraceæ,　　Plate ii.

herbs with white or coloured milky juice — leaves alternate, simple or lobed, and exstipulate ; flowers regular, fugaceous, and usually crumpled and nodding in bud ; sepals two, occasionally three, deciduous ; petals four, rarely five or six ; stamens many, free, and hypogynous ; fruit capsular or pod-shaped.

Plantaginaceæ,　　Plate xxi.

herbs with undeveloped stems — leaves radical, spreading, and entire ; flowers in spikes, sometimes monœcious ; calyx in four ; corolla very thin in four ; stamens four on corolla and elongated ; carpel solitary, superior, with a single stigma.

Plumbaginaceæ,　　Plate xxi.

shrubby herbs — leaves radical or alternate ; calyx in five, tubular and membranous ; corolla in five, regular ; stamens five, on the corolla ; styles five ; stigmas five ; carpel solitary and superior.

Polemoniaceæ,　　Plate xviii.

herbs — leaves generally pinnate and alternate ; calyx in five ; corolla in five ; stamens five, on the corolla ; ovary superior ; fruit a capsule, three-celled, three-valved, with the valves separating from the axis.

Polygalaceæ,　　Plate iv.

herbs — leaves simple, alternate, and without stipules ; flowers irregular ; sepals five, the two inner petaloid ; petals three, four, or five — one longer than the rest ; stamens eight, in two bundles, hypogynous ; capsule two-celled.

Polygonaceæ,　　Plate xxii.

herbs with swollen joints in the stem — leaves alternate with sheathing stipules ; perianth in five, free, divided, the segments often in a double row ; flowers mostly bisexual ; stamens five to eight ; ovary superior, with two or more styles or sessile stigmas ; fruit a flattened or triangular nut, usually enclosed in the sepals.

Portulaceæ,　　Plate x.

succulent herbs — leaves opposite ; sepals two, rarely three or five, coherent at base, imbricated in æstivation ; petals five, inserted into the base of the calyx ; stamens of uncertain number, generally three or five, perigynous ; ovary superior, single-celled.

Primulaceæ,　　Plate xxi.

herbs — leaves simple, opposite, or alternate ; flowers regular ; calyx in four to seven ; corolla in four to seven ; stamens in four to seven, on corolla, and opposite its

Primulaceæ, Plate xxi (*cont.*).

segments ; ovary unilocular, with a free central placenta, bearing numerous ovules, each with two coats ; fruit a many-seeded capsule.

Ranunculaceæ,   Plate i.

herbs, or a climbing shrub, with colourless, acrid juice — leaves generally deeply divided, and nearly always alternate ; occasionally with dilated sheathing petioles ; flowers regular or irregular ; sepals three, five, or six, green or petaloid ; petals five or more, free and often irregular ; stamens twelve or more (except in *Myosurus*, which has five), hypogynous ; anthers adnate and mostly reversed.

Resedaceæ,   Plate iv.

herbs—leaves alternate, without stipules ; flowers oblique and greenish ; sepals four, five, or six, narrow, persistent ; petals four, five, or six, regular, lacerated ; stamens ten or more, hypogynous, on a glandular, irregular disk ; ovary three-lobed, single-celled.

Restiaceæ,   Plate xxvii.

aquatic herbs—leaves generally imperfect ; stems generally with sheaths slit in the side ; flowers separated by bracts ; mono-cotyledon ; perianth two to six-parted ; stamens two or three, adherent to the inner perianth segments ; ovule solitary and pendulous.

Rhamnaceæ,   Plate vi.

shrubs—leaves simple and usually alternate; flowers small and greenish ; calyx four or five-cleft, valvate in æstivation ; petals four or five, on the top of the calyx tube and alternate with its lobes ; stamens four or five, opposite the petals, perigynous ; ovary superior, three-celled ; seeds solitary and erect.

Rosaceæ,   Plate viii.

shrubs or herbs—leaves alternate, with a stipule on each side of the base of the petiole ; calyx four or five-lobed, free or adherent with the ovary ; petals five, equal ; stamens vary in number, generally more than twelve, perigynous, and curved inwards in æstivation ; ovary superior, two-celled ; fruit various, but never a legume.

Rubiaceæ,   Plate xiii.

herbs, shrubs, or trees—in this country herbaceous plants ; with square stems and leaves in whorls—calyx and corolla each in four or five ; stamens four or five on the corolla, between its divisions ; ovary inferior, two-celled, with solitary erect ovules and two styles.

Salicaceæ,   Plate xxiii.

trees—leaves simple and alternate : flowers in catkins ; perianth none ; stamens two to thirty ; style one or none ; stigmas two, entire or cleft ; fruit leathery, many-seeded, and not in a cup.

Santalaceæ,   Plate xxii.

trees, shrubs, or herbaceous plants—leaves entire, alternate, and without stipules ; perianth in three or five, valvate in bud, and adnate with ovary ; stamens three or five, opposite to the perianth segments; ovary inferior, single-celled, with one to four ovules pendulous from near the top of a free central placenta.

Saxifragaceæ,   Plate x.

herbs, small, and mostly mountainous—flowers unsymmetrical ; calyx in four or five, often a tube wholly or in part adnate with the ovary ; petals four or five or wanting ; stamens five or ten, distinct and perigynous; ovary superior; carpels united into a pistil with two many-seeded cells and two diverging styles.

Scleranthaceæ,   Plate x.

tufted herbs—leaves opposite and connate ; flowers axillary ; calyx in four or five ; petals wanting ; stamens ten or less, peri-gynous ; ovary superior.

Scrophulariaceæ,   Plate xviii.

herbs—leaves generally opposite but irregular ; flowers irregular ; calyx in four or five ; corolla in four or five, imbricated in bud and irregular ; stamens 2 or 4, or else 5, rarely equal, generally two longer than the others ; ovary superior ; fruit a capsule.

Solanaceæ,   Plate xviii.

herbs—with colourless juice ; leaves alternate and without stipules ; flowers often extra axillary ; calyx in four or five ; corolla in five ; stamens five, on the corolla, and alternate with its segments ; carpels united into a superior two-celled many-seeded pistil.

Tamariscaceæ,   Plate ix.

shrubs—with twiggy branches and scale-like leaves ; flowers in lateral spikes, small and regular ; calyx in four or five ; petals four or five, rising from the base of the calyx ; stamens four, five, eight, or ten, perigynous ; ovary superior.

Thymelaceæ,   Plate xxii.

shrubs—leaves entire and without stipules ; perianth free, tubular, and in four or five ; stamens eight, inserted upon the tube ; anthers two-celled, opening longitudinally ; ovary superior, one-celled, with one pendulous ovule ; style one ; stigma one, undivided ; fruit fleshy and indehiscent.

Tiliaceæ,   Plate vi.

trees—leaves lop-sided, alternate, and with stipules ; flowers regular and inconspicuous, springing from a lanceolate leafy bract ; sepals four or five, valvate in æstivation, deciduous : petals four or five, often with a depression at the base ; stamens many, hypogynous, not united as in Malvaceæ.

Trilliaceæ,   Plate xxvi,

herbs—leave whorled, ovate, and with netted veins ; flowers terminal and solitary; monocotyledon ; perianth six or ten, in two rows, outer herbaceous, inner filiform; stamens six or ten ; ovary superior.

Typhaceæ,   Plate xxvii.

marsh herbs —stems without nodes ; leaves sessile, parallel - nerved, and ensiform ; flowers in dense conspicuous heads ; monocotyledon ; perianth wanting ; stamens many ; seed solitary and pendulous.

Ulmaceæ,   Plate xxiii.

trees—leaves scabious, lop-sided, distichous, and stipuled ; flowers perfect ; fruit winged ; perianth in three to eight parts, generally five, segments imbricated in bud ; stamens five, opposite segments of perianth and inserted into its base ; anthers two-celled ; ovary free ; stigmas two, distinct and elongated.

Umbelliferæ,   Plates xii., xiii.

herbs, generally with fistular stems—leaves alternate, without stipules, deeply divided, and sheathing at the base ; flowers regular, in umbels, and mostly white ; calyx in five, teeth minute or often wanting ; petals five, often unequal ; stamens five, epigynous, alternate with the petals, and springing with them from a thick fleshy disk at the base of the two styles ; seeds one in each of the two carpels, adherent, pendulous, and albuminous.

Urticaceæ,   Plate xxiii.

herbs—leaves with stipules, often stinging, and sometimes milky ; flowers monœcious, diœcious, or polygamous ; perianth four

Urticaceæ, Plate xxiii (*cont.*).

or five, regular, free from the ovary, of absent ; stamens four or five, hypogynous, and uncoiling elastically ; ovary free, single-celled.

Vacciniaceæ,   Plate xvii.

shrubs—leaves alternate ; flowers solitary and regular ; calyx in four or five ; corolla in four or five ; stamens eight or ten, on the inferior ovary ; fruit a berry.

Valerianaceæ,   Plate xiii.

herbs, generally aromatic—leaves opposite and without stipules ; calyx five, with one limb becoming membranous or pappose ; corolla five, monopetalous ; stamens three, on the corolla ; carpels solitary, inferior, with one pendulous ovule.

Verbenaceæ,   Plate xix.

herbs—leaves opposite and three-toothed ; calyx tubular ; corolla tubular and bifid ; stamens on the corolla, two long and two short ; ovary four-celled and superior ; fruit a capsule of four nutlets.

Violaceæ,   Plate iv.

herbs—leaves alternate and with stipules ; flowers irregular and axillary ; sepals five, persistent and imbricate ; petals five, unequal, with the lower one spurred at the base ; stamens five, hypogynous, with the connective produced above the anther cells ; ovary tripartite and single-celled.

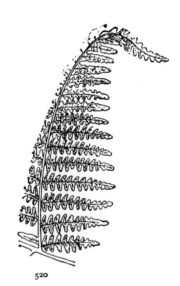

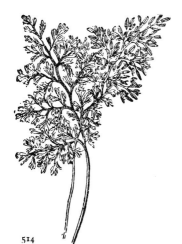

THE GENERA.

IN this List only such particulars are given as are needed to distinguish one genus from another. In the illustrations the distinctive marks of each genus are given in diagrammatic form. For the characteristics of the orders reference must be made to the preceding index; the characteristics of the species are given in the index that follows.

514

ACERACEÆ. Plate vi.

Acer,

sepals, four to nine; petals, four to nine; stamens, five to twelve, generally eight, on a ring beneath the ovary; ovary bilobed, and fruit a samaia—(the maple and sycamore).

ALISMACEÆ.
Plate xxvii.

Actinocarpus,

flat leaves, large flowers, carpels joined at base—(the star fruit).

Alisma,

flat leaves, large flowers, carpels free and many—(the water plantain).

ALISMACEÆ.

Butomus,

leaves on a sharply triangular stem; flowers red—(the flowering rush).

Sagittaria,

arrow-shaped leaves, carpels free, stamens many—(the arrowhead).

Scheuchzeria,

linear leaves; bent segments of the perianth.

ALISMACEÆ.

Triglochin,

linear leaves; erect segments of the perianth—(the arrow grass).

AMARANTHACEÆ.
Plate xxii.

Amaranthus,

flowers green, very small, and unisexual; stamens from three to five; perianth three to five.

AMARYLLIDACEÆ
Plate xxv.

Galanthus,

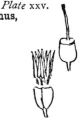

perianth of unequal segments and without a crown—(the snowdrop).

AMARYLLIDACEÆ.
Leucojum,

periantn of equal segments, and without a crown—(the snowflake).

Narcissus,

a crown in the perianth—(the daffodil).

APOCYNACEÆ.
Plate xvii.
Vinca,

calyx, five ; corolla, five, and twisted in bud; anthers,two-celled;ovary superior;leaves opposite, entire ; purple flowers, with the angles of a pentagon — (the peri-winkle).

AQUIFOLIACEÆ.
Plate xvii.
Ilex,

sepals, four to six, imbricated in bud ; stamens, four to five, alternating with lobes of corolla;fruit,a scarlet berry; spiny evergreen leaves—(the holly).

ARACEÆ. Plate xxvii.
Acorus,

leaf-like scape, much longer than the spadix ; a tall water plant, with fragrant sword-shaped leaves—(the sweet-flag).

Arum,

leaves spear-shaped or tri-angular — (the lords and ladies).

ARALIACEÆ.
Plate xi.
Adoxa,

herbaceous stem ; monopeta-lous corolla ; cubical head of five flowers—(the mos-chatel).

Hedera,

woody stem ; five petals ; plant, a climber—(the ivy).

ARISTOLOCHIA-CEÆ. Plate xxii.

Aristolochia,

perianth tubular, curved, with mouth dilated on one side ; flowers in groups ; six sta-mens ; a creeping plant—(the birthwort).

Asarum,

perianth bell-shaped ; twelve stamens ; flowers solitary ; plant with two large shining leaves only—(the asara-bacca).

BALSAMINACEÆ.
Plate vi.
Impatiens,

sepals, three, two nearly cir-cular, one horn-like ; petals, five ; stamens, five, with short filaments all in a ring enclosing ovary ; capsule valves elastic ; alternate leaves—(the balsam)

BERBERIDACEÆ.
Plate i.

Berberis,

petals, six ; sepals, in a double row, six ; stamens, six ; anthers open by top valves and turn upwards — (the barberry).

BETULACEÆ.
Plate xxiii.

Alnus,

stamens, four ; male catkins much longer than the others ; fruit without wings —(the alder).

Betula,

stamens, eight at least ; fruit with wings—(the birch).

BORAGINACEÆ.
Plate xx.

Division A—
having scales in the throat of the corolla.

Division B—
having no scales in the throat of the corolla.

Division A—
Series i.. having nuts affixed to the base of the style.
Series ii., having nuts affixed to a disk, with a space surrounded by a tumid ring at the base.

BORAGINACEÆ.
Division A.
Series I.

Asperugo,

calyx five-cleft and flattened, with alternate smaller teeth —(the madwort).

Cynoglossum,

calyx, with five deep equal cuts—(the hound's tongue).

Series II,

Anchusa,

stamens included ; funnel-shaped corolla, with a straight tube ; a bract under each flower—(the alkanet).

Borago,

segments of calyx very deep ; corolla wheel-shaped, with short tube ; stamens exserted, forming a cone — (the borage).

BORAGINACEÆ.

Lycopsis,

funnel-shaped corolla, with a curved tube—(the bugloss).

Myosotis,

salver-shaped corolla, contorted in the bud ; racemes without bracts—(the forget-me-not).

Symphytum,

cylindrical bell-shaped corolla, closed by a high cone of awl-like scales — (the comfrey).

Division B.

Echium

deeply-cut irregular corolla— (the viper's bugloss).

BORAGINACEÆ.
Lithospermum,

regular corolla, sometimes with five tiny scales in throat; calyx divided to the base; stamens included; stony seeds; flowers either yellow, white, or blue—(the gromwell).

Mertensia,

regular corolla; stamens protruded—(the smooth gromwell).

Pulmonaria,

regular corolla; calyx tubular, the lobes not reaching to the middle; stamens included; flowers either purple or pink—(the lungwort).

CAMPANULACEÆ.
Plate xvi.
Division A—
    having the corolla irregular.

Lobelia,

corolla tube slit on one side; the anthers syngenesious,

CAMPANULACEÆ.
Division B—
    having the corolla regular.

Campanula,

bell-shaped corolla—(the bell flower).

Jasione,

wheel-shaped corolla, with the anthers cohering at their base; small flowers —(the sheep's scabions).

Phyteuma,

wheel-shaped corolla, with the anthers free at their base—(the rampion).

CAPRIFOLIACEÆ.
Plate xiii.

Linnæa,

a single stigma; four stamens; and a regular corolla; two flowers on the stalk—(the very small plant so modestly chosen by Linnæus to bear his name).

CAPRIFOLIACEÆ.
Lonicera,

a single stigma; five stamens; and an irregular corolla— (the honeysuckle).

Sambucus,

three stigmas; five stamens wheel-shaped corolla; pinnate leaves—(the elder).

Viburnum,

three stigmas; five stamens; funnel-shaped corolla; simple leaves— (the guelder rose).

CARYOPHYL-
LACEÆ. *Plate* v.

Division A—
    having ten stamens, and the sepals connected into a tube.

Division B—
    having less than ten stamens, and the sepals not connected into a tube.

Division B—
    Series i., with stipules to leaves.

    Series ii., without stipules.

CARYOPHYL-LACEÆ.

Division A.

Dianthus,

styles, two ; calyx with bracts at base—(the pink).

Lychnis,

styles, five—(the campion).

Saponaria,

styles, two ; calyx without bracts—(the soapwort).

Silene,

styles, three or four — (the catchfly).

Division B.
Series I.

Spergula,

styles, five—(the spurrey).

CARYOPHYL-LACEÆ.

Spergularia,

styles, three — (the seaside spurrey).

Series II.

Arenaria,

petals, five ; entire or slightly emarginate ; stamens, ten or less ; styles, three ; flowers all perfect — (the sandwort).

Cerastium,

petals, bifid ; stamens, ten or less ; styles, four or five—(the mouse-ear chickweed).

Cherleria,

petals, entire, but frequently absent ; stamens, ten : styles, three—(the cyphel).

CARYOPHYL-LACEÆ.

Holosteum,

petals toothed ; stamens, five or less ; styles, three—(the jagged chickweed).

Honckenya,

petals, five, entire ; stamens, ten or less ; styles, two or three ; flowers never perfect—(the sea purslane).

Moenchia,

petals, four ; sepals, four ; stamens, four; styles, three.

Sagina,

stamens, ten or less ; petals, five or less, and shorter than the sepals : styles, four or five—(the pearlwort).

Stellaria,

petals, bifid ; stamens, ten ; styles, three—(the stitchwort).

CELASTRACEÆ.
Plate vi.

Euonymus,

petals, four; stamens, four; capsule, three to five angled; seeds coated with fleshy scarlet arillus; branches angular; bark very green —(the spindle tree).

CHENOPODIACEÆ.
Plate xxii.

Division A—
  diœcious plants with perfect flowers.

Division B—
  unisexual plants with imperfect flowers.

Beta,

perianth five-cleft; stamens, five; stigmas, two; fruit adhering to perianth; leaves flat—(the beet).

Chenopodium,

fruit not adhering to perianth; leaves flat — (the goosefoot).

Salicornia,

jointed stem, without leaves —(the glasswort).

CHENOPODIACEÆ.
Salsola,

leaves cylindrical and spinous —(the saltwort).

Suæda,

leaves semi-cylindrical and not spinous—(the sea-blite).

Division B.

Atriplex,

fruit not adhering to perianth —(the orache).

Obione,

fruit adhering to perianth—(the sea purslane).

CISTACEÆ.
Plate iv.

Helianthemum,

sepals, five, the two outer small or wanting; petals, five, deciduous; stamens numerous; capsule with three valves — (the rock rose).

COMPOSITÆ.
Plates xiv., xv., xvi.

Division A—
  florets all ligulate and perfect (as in the dandelion).

Division B—
  florets of the disk all tubular; florets of the ray often ligulate, and of a different colour to those of the disk (as in the daisy).

Division C—
  florets of the disk all tubular; florets of the ray often ligulate, and of the same colour as those of the disk (as in the coltsfoot).

Division D—
  florets all tubular; the style thickened below its branches (as in the thistle).

Division A—
  Series i., without a pappus.
  Series ii., with a pappus like a crown of many broad scales.
  Series iii., with a feathery pappus and a scaly receptacle.
  Series iv., with a feathery pappus and receptacle without scales.
  Series v., with a hairy pappus.
  Series vi., with the hairs of the pappus bristly and turning brown.

Division B—
  Series i., without a pappus.
  Series ii., with a pappus.

Division C—
  Series i., without a pappus.
  Series ii., pappus not feathery.
  Series iii., pappus feathery; flowers preceding leaves.
  Series iv., pappus feathery; flowers appearing after the leaves; stems leafy; heads radiant.
  Series v., pappus feathery; flowers appearing after the leaves; stems leafy; heads discoid.

Division D—
  Series i., smooth leaves.
  Series ii., spiny leaves.

COMPOSITÆ,

Division A.

Series I.

Lapsana,

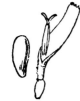

heads eight to twelve-flowered —(the swine's cress).

Series II.

Arnoseris,

involucre in one row; yellow terminal flowers — (the nipple wort).

Cichorium,

involucre in two rows; blue axillary flowers — (the chicory).

Series III.

Hypochæris,

pappus in two rows, the outer short and bristly, the inner long and feathery — (the cat's ear).

COMPOSITÆ.

Series IV.

Helminthia,

involucre simple; bracts leafy —(the ox tongue).

Leontodon,

involucre imbricate — (the hawkbit).

Picris,

involucre simple; bracts linear.

Tragopogon,

involucre simple; pappus interwoven in the ray—(the goatsbeard)

COMPOSITÆ.

Series V.

Borkhausia,

fruit beaked and round; leafy stem.

Crepis,

fruit not beaked but round —(the hawksbeard).

Lactuca,

fruit beaked and compressed; leaves pinnatifid; flowers blue—(the lettuce).

Sonchus,

fruit not beaked but compressed — (the yellow sow thistle).

COMPOSITÆ.
Taraxacum,

fruit beaked and suddenly contracted ; stem leafless— (the dandelion).

Series VI.
Hieracium,

yellow flowers — (the hawk weed).

Mulgedium,

blue flowers — (the blue sow thistle).

Division B.
Series I.
Anthemis,

scaly receptacle—(the camomile).

COMPOSITÆ.
Bellis,

receptacle conical and naked ; involucre of two rows of equal obtuse scales — (the daisy).

Chrysanthemum,

receptacle flat, or convex, and naked ; fruit rounded ; involucre hemispherical — (the ox-eye, the yellow species of which has both sets of florets of the same colour).

Matricaria,

receptacle conical or convex, and naked ; fruit angular ; involucre nearly flat—(the feverfew).

Series II.
Aster,

one row of ray florets—(the michaelmas daisy).

COMPOSITÆ.
Erigeron,

many rows of ray florets— (the flea bane).

Division C.
Series I.
Achillea,

receptacle scaly ; heads radiant—(the yarrow).

Artemisia,

receptacle not scaly ; head discoidal—(the wormwood).

Diotis,

two ears in the fruit ; receptacle scaly ; heads discoidal —(the cotton weed).

COMPOSITÆ.

Tanacetum,

receptacle not scaly; fruit angular with a broad epi-gynous disk crowned with a slight membranous bor-der—(the tansy).

Series II.

Bidens,

pappus of five or fewer stiff bristles — (the bur-mari-gold).

Galinsoga,

pappus of broad hairy scales.

Series III.

Petasites,

flowers in heads; leaves rad-ical—(the butter-bur).

COMPOSITÆ.

Tussilago,

flowers solitary; leaves radi-cal—(the coltsfoot).

Series IV.

Cineraria,

involucre of one row of equal scales—(the fleawort).

Doronicum,

involucre of two or three rows of equal scales — (the leopard's bane).

Inula,

involucre imbricated and in many rows; anthers with bristles at the base—(the elecampane).

COMPOSITÆ

Senecio,

involucre in one row with several small scales at the base—(the groundsel).

Solidago,

imbricated involucre, but an-thers without bristles—(the golden rod)

Series V.

Antennaria,

pappus clavate — (the ever-lasting).

Chrysocoma,

bracts herbaceous; linear leaves—(the goldilocks).

H

COMPOSITÆ.

Eupatorium,

reddish-purple flowers—(the hemp agrimony).

Filago,

hard, dry bracts, intermixing with the outer florets ; conical receptacle.

Gnaphalium,

hard dry bracts ; flat receptacle—(the cudweed).

Division D.

Series I.

Arctium,

hooked points to the bracts— (the burdock).

COMPOSITÆ.

Centaurea,

hookless bracts ; pappus shorter than the fruit— (the knapweed).

Saussurea,

hookless bracts ; pappus longer than the fruit ; anthers with bristles at their base.

Serratula,

hookless bracts ; pappus longer than the fruit ; anthers without bristles – (the saw wort).

Series II.

Carduus,

bracts all spinous ; fruit compressed—(the thistle).

COMPOSITÆ.

Carlina,

outer row of bracts spinous ; inner row chaffy and straw-coloured, and spreading like a ray—(the carline thistle).

Onopordum,

bracts all spinous ; fruit with four ribs—(the Scotch thistle).

CONIFERÆ.
Plate xxv.

Juniperus,

fruit, a green berry, containing three seeds ; leaves, three in a whorl — (the juniper bush).

Pinus,

fruit, a woody cone, containing many seeds ; leaves fasciated in pairs— the Scotch fir tree).

Taxus,

fruit, a pink berry, containing one seed ; leaves in two ranks—(the yew).

CONVOLVULACEÆ.
Plate xviii.
Convolvulus,

trumpet-shaped corolla, with five plaits and five lobes; arrow-shaped leaves—(the way wind).

Cuscuta,

a parasite without leaves—(the dodder).

CORNACEÆ.
Plate xi.
Cornus,

petals, four, inserted into the top of the calyx; sepals, four, attached to the ovary; stamens, four, inserted with the petals; ovary, two-celled; fruit, a berry-like drupe—(the dogwood).

CRASSULACEÆ.
Plate x.
Cotyledon,

petals, five, united at the base; stamens, ten—(the pennywort).

CRASSULACEÆ.
Sedum,

petals, five or less, not united at the base: stamens, ten or more—(the stonecrop).

Sempervivum,

petals, ten or more; stamens, many—(the house leek).

Tillæa,

petals, three or four; stamens, three or four.

CRUCIFERÆ.
Plates ii., iii.

Division A—
with fruit as a silicle or pouch.

Division B—
with fruit as a silique or pod.

Division A—
Series i., pouch single-jointed.
Series ii., pouch double-jointed.
Series iii., pouch bi-valved and laterally compressed.
Series iv., pouch bi-valved and dorsally compressed.
Series v., pouch bi-valved, and more or less ovate.

Division B—
Series i., pod jointed.
Series ii , pod with beaks.
Series iii., pod without beaks or joints.

CRUCIFERÆ.
Division A.
Series I.
Isatis,

pouch flat, and three times as long as it is broad—(the woad).

Series II.
Cakile,

upper joint of pouch sword-shaped and deciduous — (the sea rocket).

Coronopus,

pouch wrinkled and broader than its length, and notched at ends—(the wart cress).

Crambe,

upper joint of pouch globose; lower joint seedless — (the sea kale).

Series III.
Capsella,

triangular pouch, valves keeled but not winged; seeds, many—(the shepherd's purse).

H 2

CRUCIFERÆ.

Hutchinsia,

elliptical pouch, valves keeled but not winged ; seeds, only two.

Iberis,

globose pouch with notches ; valves winged ; cells single-seeded—(the candy tuft).

Lepidium,

ovate pouch ; valves keeled ; cells single-seeded — (the pepperwort).

Teesdalia,

roundish pouch, notched, with valves keeled below and winged above ; cells two-seeded.

Thlaspi,

valves winged at the back ; cells many-seeded — (the penny cress).

CRUCIFERÆ.

Series IV.

Alyssum,

cells two or more seeded ; flowers yellow—(the madwort).

Koniga,

cells single-seeded ; flowers white.

Series V.

Camelina,

valves single - nerved and inflated ; cells many-seeded —(the gold of pleasure).

Cochlearia,

valves very convex and veined, and cells many-seeded ; leaves spoon-shaped—(the scurvy grass).

Draba,

valves slightly convex, and cells many-seeded in two rows—(the whitlow grass).

CRUCIFERÆ.

Subularia,

valves boat-shaped ; cells four-seeded—(the awl wort).

Division B.

Series I.

Raphanus,

sepals erect ; fruit without valves or dissepiment ; single-seeded joints—(the radish).

Series II.

Brassica,

sepals erect ; seeds in a single row, globose—(the cabbage

Diplotaxis,

sepals spreading ; pod compressed ; seeds in two rows —(the rocket.)

CRUCIFERÆ.

Sinapis,

sepals spreading; seeds in a single row—(the mustard).

Series III.

Arabis,

compressed linear pod, with flat valves, having one or more veins—(the rock cress).

Barbarea,

four-angled pod; valves with a prominent rib; flowers yellow—(the winter cress).

Cardamine,

compressed linear pod and flat valves without veins —(the cuckoo flower).

Cheiranthus,

two sepals bulging at the base; flattened pod, valves, with a prominent nerve— (the wall flower).

CRUCIFERÆ.

Dentaria,

compressed lanceolate tapering pod, with flat nerveless valves—(the coral wort).

Erysimum,

four-sided pod, with keeled valves; flowers white—(the treacle mustard).

Hesperis,

four-sided pod, with nerved valves; stigma bilobed, the lobes erect, elliptical and obtuse; flowers lilac—(the dame's violet).

Matthiola,

rounded linear pod; stigma gibbous or horned at back —(the stock).

Nasturtium,

short linear pod; convex nerveless valves; seeds in two irregular rows—(the water cress).

CRUCIFERÆ.

Sisymbrium,

rounded hexagonal linear pod, with convex veined valves; seeds not striated—(the hedge mustard).

CUCURBITACEÆ.

Plate ix.

Bryonia,

calyx, five; corolla, five: stamens, five, in three bundles; trifid style; fruit a globose trilocular red berry—(the white bryony).

CUPULIFERÆ.

Plate xxiii.

Division I—

barren flowers in a globose catkin.

Division II—

barren flowers in a long catkin.

Division I—

Fagus,

fertile flowers, two together within a four-lobed involucre; stigmas, three; nuts three cornered—(the beech).

CUPULIFERÆ.
Division II—
Carpinus,

fertile flowers in a loose catkin; stigmas, two — (the
hornbeam).

Corylus,

stigmas, two, bright crimson;
male catkins long and pendulous—(the hazel).

Quercus,

stigmas, three; fruit, an acorn
—(the oak).

CYPERACEÆ.
Plate xxviii.

Division I—
  Imperfect flowers.
Division II—
  Perfect flowers; glumes in
  two ranks.
Division III—
  Perfect flowers; imbricated
  glumes.

Division I—
Carex,

fruit in the perigone — (the
sedge).

CYPERACEÆ.
Kobresia.

fruit not in the perigone.

Division II—
Cyperus,

spikelets double ranked;
glumes of one valve, numerous and nearly all with
flowers—(the galingale).

Schœnus,

spikelets double ranked;
glumes six, seven, eight,
or nine: the lower ones
small and empty—(the bog
rush).

Division III.
Blysmus,

bristles within the glume;
alternate spikelets.

CYPERACEÆ.
Cladium,

no bristles; lower glumes
empty—(the twig rush).

Eleocharis,

bristles within the glume; one
terminal spikelet — (the
spike rush).

Eriophorum,

bristles, six or less, longer
than the glume—(the cot-
ton grass).

Isolepis,

no bristles; lower glumes as
full as the upper—(the mud
rush).

CYPERACEÆ.
Rhyncospora,

bristles within the glume; spikelets in an ovate head— (the beak rush).

Scirpus,

bristles, six, within the glume; lateral, fascicled spikelets —(the club rush).

DIOSCOREACEÆ.
Plate xxvi.
Tamus,

perianth bell-shaped; limb in six parts; six stamens; diœcious; female with perianth adherent to ovary and persistent—(the black bryony).

DIPSACEÆ.
Plate xiv.
Dipsacus,

receptacle with rigid scales; fruit with four sides and eight depressions — (the teasel).

DIPSACEÆ.
Knautia,

receptacle hairy, without scales; fruit with four sides and four depressions; more than seven bristles on calyx limb.

Scabiosa,

receptacle scaly; fruit cylindrical—(the scabious).

DROSERACEÆ.
Plate iv.
Drosera,

calyx, five; petals, five; stamens five; styles three, four, or five; glandular leaves; insectivorous plant —(the sundew).

ELATINACEÆ.
Plate iv.
Elatine,

calyx, petals, styles, and capsules, each three or four; stamens, three or four, or six or eight; small aquatic plant—(the waterwort).

ELEAGNACEÆ.
Plate xxii.
Hippophäe,

diœcious; perianth of two leaves adhering by their points: perigone tubular and cloven at the summit— (the sea buckthorn).

EMPETRACEÆ.
Plate xxii.
Empetrum,

diœcious; calyx, three-parted; petals, three; stamens, three; stigma with six or nine rays—(the crowberry).

EQUISETACEÆ.
Plate xxxii.
Equisetum,

leafless branched plants, with striated fistular stem—(the horsetail).

ERICACEÆ.
Plate xvii.
Division A—
with fleshy fruits.
Division B—
with dry fruits.
Division A.
Arbutus,

disk hypogynous; cells many-seeded —(the strawberry tree).

ERICACEÆ.

Arctostaphylos,

disk hypogynous; cells, single-seeded — (the bear berry).

Division B.

Andromeda,

corolla, ovate and deciduous; stamens, ten; flowers, pink; leaves lanceolate.

Calluna,

corolla, persistent; calyx, double; leaves opposite— (the heather).

Erica,

corolla persistent; calyx simple—(the heath).

Loiseleuria,

corolla, bell-shaped and deciduous; stamens, five; leaves very small and opposite—(the azalea).

ERICACEÆ.

Menziesia,

corolla, swollen and deciduous; leaves white underneath; stamens, ten.

Monotropa,

calyx coloured; corolla of four or five petals, each with a hooded nectariferous base; flowers turned all one way; a leafless parasitic plant —(the bird's-nest).

Pyrola,

calyx green; style, five-lobed; leaves pear-shaped and almost radical—(the winter green).

EUPHORBIACEÆ.

Plate xxiii.

Buxus,

stamens, four; an evergreen shrub—(the box).

EUPHORBIACEÆ.

Euphorbia,

stamens, many; pistils enclosed in calyx-like bracts— (the spurge

Mercurialis,

stamens, nine to twelve; perianth three-parted — (the dog's mercury).

FILICES. *Plate* xxxiii.

Division A—

the sori on spikes.

Division B—

sori on the back, without indusium.

Division C—

sori on the back, with indusium.

Division D—

sori at margin, covered by an elongated part of the frond.

Division E—

sori at margin, terminating a vein.

Division C—

Series i., sori nearly circular.

Series ii., sori oblong or linear.

FILICES.
Division A.
Botrychium,

leaves entire; vernation straight; spikes in panicles —(the moon wort).

Ophioglossum,

leaves entire; vernation straight; spikes simple— (the adder's tongue).

Osmunda,

leaves bipinnate; vernation circinate; branched spike terminating the frond—(the royal fern).

Division B.
Ceterach,

sori elongate; the whole back of the frond covered with chaffy scales — (the scale fern).

Gymnogramma,

sori linear.

FILICES.
Polypodium,

sori circular — (the polypody).

Division C.
Series I.
Cystopteris,

indusium like a small bladder attached by its broad hooded base, and turning back at the point—(the bladder fern).

Lastræa,

indusium reniform, attached by the sinus; veins distinct after leaving the mid-rib— (the male fern).

Polystichum,

indusium circular, attached by its centre; veins distinct after leaving the mid-rib— (the shield fern).

FILICES.
Pseudathyrium,

indusium crescent - shaped, attached across the vein by their inner edge.

Woodsia,

indusium underneath the sori.

Series II.
Asplenium,

sori single, lying in the direction of the veins; indusium unfringed — (the spleenwort).

Athyrium,

sori single, often curved, lying in short lines; indusium fringed—(the lady fern).

Scolopendrium,

sori double, confluent along their whole length; simple fronds—(the hart's tongue)

FILICES.

Division D.

Adiantum,

sori oblong or roundish; fronds all similar; veins dichotomous—(the maiden-hair).

Allosorus,

two kinds of fronds; fronds bipinnate or tripinnate and triangular and soft—(the parsley fern).

Blechnum,

two kinds of fronds; fronds pinnate and lanceolate, and somewhat rigid—(the hard fern).

Pteris,

sori continuous round the margin—(the bracken).

FILICES.

Division E.

Hymenophyllum,

pellucid fronds; two-valved covering to sori—(the film fern).

Trichomanes,

cup-shaped covering to sori —(the bristle fern).

FRANKENIACEÆ.

Plate iv.

Frankenia,

style three-fid; stigma on inner side of oblong lobes; leaves revolute at margin—(the sea heath).

FUMARIACEÆ.

Plate ii.

Corydalis,

fruit long and many-seeded crested seeds.

FUMARIACEÆ.

Fumaria,

fruit round and single-seeded; seeds without a crest—(the fumitory).

GENTIANACEÆ.

Plate xvii.

Division A—
with alternate leaves.

Division B—
with opposite leaves.

Division A.

Menyanthes,

corolla funnel-shaped and white; leaves ternate – (the buckbean).

Villarsia,

corolla wheel-shaped and yellow; leaves heart-shaped and floating, and wavy at the edges.

Division B.

Chlora,

calyx eight-cleft; corolla wheel-shaped; stamens, eight; leaves glaucous and perfoliate — (the yellow wort).

GENTIANACEÆ.

Cicendia,

corolla bell-shaped ; stamens, four ; stigma undivided.

Erythræa,

corolla funnel - shaped and rose - coloured ; stamens, five ; anthers twisted ; stigmas, two—(the centaury).

Gentiana,

corolla salver-shaped ; style persistent—(the gentian).

GERANIACEÆ.
Plate vi.

Erodium,

stamens, ten, five of which are shorter than the rest and have no anthers ; fruit with a smooth recurved awn—(the stork's bill).

Geranium,

stamens, ten, five of which are shorter than the rest, but all have anthers ; fruit with a bearded spiral awn —(the crane's bill).

GRAMINEÆ.
Plates xxix., xxx.

Division A—
sessile spikelets in a compound spike.

Division B—
sessile spikelets in a simple spike.

Division C—
stalked spikelets, with one perfect floret.

Division D—
stalked spikelets, with one perfect floret, and the others rudimentary.

Division E—
stalked spikelets, with two or more perfect florets.

Division A—
Series i., spikes upright.
Series ii., spike spreading.

Division B—
Series i., spikelets solitary.
Series ii., spikelets in groups.

Division C—
Series i., spikelets in a spike.
Series ii., s p i k e l e t s in a panicle.

Division D—
Series i., spikelets in a spike.
Series ii., spikelets in a panicle.

Division E—
Series i., florets awned.
Series ii., florets not awned.

Division A.
Series I.

Spartina,

glumes unequal, the upper long and acuminate ; styles united half way up—(the cord grass).

GRAMINEÆ.
Series II.

Cynodon,

glumes equal — (the dog's-tooth grass).

Digitaria,

glumes unequal ; no bristles at base of spikelets—(the finger grass).

Panicum,
glumes unequal : bristles at base of spikelets — (the panic grass).

Division B.
Series I.

Brachypodium,

spikelets broadside to rachis ; glumes unequal—(the false brome).

Knappia,
spikelets unilateral and single flowered.

Lepturus,

spikelets bi-lateral and single flowered—(the hard grass).

GRAMINEÆ.

Lolium,

spikelets edgeways to rachis and many - flowered—(the rye grass).

Nardus,

spikelets in a two-rowed spike; no glumes—(the mat grass).

Triticum,

spikelets broadside to rachis; glumes equal—(the wheat grass).

Series II.

Elymus,

spikelets with two or more flowers—(the lyme grass).

GRAMINEÆ.

Hordeum,

spikelets with single flowers —(the barley).

Division C.
Series I.

Alopecurus,

awns to paleæ—(the fox tail).

Phleum,

no awns to paleæ — (the cat's tail).

Series II.

Agrostis,

larger glumes below; no awns to outer paleæ—(the bent grass).

GRAMINEÆ.

Apera,

larger glumes above; awns to outer paleæ.

Calamagrostis,

glumes equal; paleæ with silky hairs — (the small **reed).**

Gastridium,

glumes acute, united and swollen at the base—(the nit grass).

Leersia,

no glumes—(the cut grass).

Milium,

glumes equal; paleæ un-awned—(the millet).

GRAMINEÆ.
Polypogon,

glumes emarginate with a long slender awn — (the beard grass).

Division D.
Series I.
Ammophila,

spike cylindrical and uninterrupted—(the marram).

Lagurus,

spike ovate ; outer palea bifid and long awned—(the hare's tail).

Phalaris,

spike ovate ; glumes equal and keeled — (the canary grass).

Setaria,

spike cylindrical and interrupted below—(the bristle grass).

GRAMINEÆ.
Series II.
Anthoxhuam,

stamens, two ; glumes unequal —(the vernal grass).

Arrhenatherum,
upper floret perfect and awned ; lower floret barren and awned—(the false oat).

Hierochloe,

upper floret perfect and unawned ; two lower ones with stamens only and unawned—(the holy grass).

Holcus,

upper floret with stamens only and awned ; lower floret perfect and awned—(the soft grass).

Division E.
Series I.
Aira,

lower palea bifid ; awn geniculate—(the hair grass).

GRAMINEÆ.
Arundo,

lower paleæ entire ; fruit free of paleæ ; spikelets hairy— (the reed).

Avena,

lower paleæ bifid ; awn twisted—(the oat)

Bromus,

lower paleæ bifid ; awn straight—(the brome).

Dactylis,

lower paleæ entire ; spikelets crowded—(the cock's foot).

GRAMINEÆ.

Festuca,

lower paleæ entire; fruit adherent to palea— (the fescue).

Koeleria,

lower paleæ entire ; fruit free of paleæ ; spikelets in interrupted spike.

Series II.

Briza,

spikelets without apparent involucre ; fruit adherent to palea — (the quaking grass).

Catabrosa,

glumes and outer paleæ eroso-truncate—(the whorl grass).

Cynosurus,

spikelets with a pectinate bract at base—(the dog's tail).

GRAMINEÆ.

Glyceria,

glumes obtuse and unequal; lower paleæ obtuse—(the meadow grass).

Melica,

glumes equal ; spikelets of two perfect florets and a club-like rudiment — (the melic).

Molinia,

glumes unequal, not veined, and shorter than the lanceolate spikelet.

Poa,

glumes acute and unequal ; outer palea compressed and keeled—(the meadow grass).

Sclerochloa,

glumes acute and unequal ; outer paleæ cylindrical below,

GRAMINEÆ.

Sesleria,

spikelets with a ciliate bract at base—(the moor grass).

Triodia,

glumes acute and unequal ; lower palea emarginate, with an intermediate tooth —(the heath grass).

GROSSULARIACEÆ

Plate x.

Ribes,

calyx five-cleft ; petals and stamens inserted at the mouth of the tube ; berry many-seeded, crowned with the persistent calyx—(the currant).

HALORAGACEÆ.

Plate ix.

Callitriche,

one stamen ; opposite leaves — (the water star wort).

HALORAGACEÆ.
Ceratophyllum,

sessile anthers, twelve and more in number ; leaves forked and in a whorl — (the horn wort).

Hippuris,

one stamen ; whorled undivided leaves—(the mare's tai).

Myriophyllum,

stamens, eight ; leaves in a whorl and divided into setaceous segments — (the water milfoil).

HYDROCHARIDA-CEÆ. Plate xxvi.
Elodea,

leaves submerged, linear in shape—(the water thyme).

Hydrocharis,

floating reniform leaves—(the frog bit).

HYDROCHARIDA-CEÆ.
Stratiotes,

leaves submerged, rigid, and sword-shaped — (the water soldier).

HYPERICACEÆ.
Plate vi.
Hypericum,

calyx, five ; petals, five ; stamens many and in groups ; styles, three or five—(the St. John's wort).

ILLECEBRACEÆ.
Plate x.
Corrigiola,

alternate leaves — (the strap wort).

Herniaria,

filiform petals ; one-seeded capsule ; opposite leaves,

ILLECEBRACEÆ
Illecebrum,

no petals ; one-seeded capsule ; opposite leaves—(the knot grass).

Polycarpon,

many-seeded capsule ; opposite leaves, in fours below— (the allseed).

IRIDACEÆ.
Plate xxv.

Division A—
having perianth of unequal segments.

Division B—
having perianth of equal segments.

Division A—
Iris,

perianth six-cleft, its alternate segments turned back ; stigma petaloid and covering the stamens ; flowers purple or yellow — (the flag).

IRIDACEÆ.

Gladiolus,

flowers crimson — (the corn flag).

Division B—

Crocus,

perianth funnel-shaped and with a long tube.

Sisyrinchium,

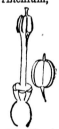

perianth with short tube; flowers blue.

Trichcnema,

perianth with short tube; scape single-flowered; a very small plant.

JUNCACEÆ.

Plate xxviii.

Juncus,

perianth glumaceous, six-leaved; filaments glabrous; capsule three-celled and many-seeded—(the rush).

Luzula,

perianth glumaceous, six-leaved; filaments glabrous; capsule single-celled, with three seeds at the base—(the wood rush).

Narthecium,

perianth coloured yellow; filaments woolly; capsule three-celled — (the bog asphodel).

LABIATÆ.

Plate xix.

Division A—

having two stamens.

Division B—

having four stamens divergent, and nearly all of equal length.

Division C—

having four stamens, two longer than the others, and the upper lip of corolla very short or absent.

Division D—

having four stamens, two longer than the others, and the upper lip of corolla longer than the stamens.

LABIATÆ.

Division D—

   Series i., calyx with two lips.

   Series ii., calyx with five teeth.

   Series iii., calyx with ten teeth.

Division A—

Lycopus,

calyx with five teeth –(the gipsy wort).

Salvia,

calyx with two lips — (the sage).

Division B—

Mentha,

corolla with four or five clefts; calyx five-cleft, almost smooth in the throat—(the mint).

Origanum,

corolla with two lips; calyx five-cleft; flowers inter-mixed with bracts in a terminal panicle — (the marjoram).

LABIATÆ.

Thymus,

corolla with two lips ; flowers in terminal heads — (the thyme).

Division C.

Ajuga,

upper lip of corolla very short, and entire or but slightly notched ; corolla bell-shaped—(the bugle).

Teucrium,

upper lip of corolla deeply bifid ; corolla tubular—(the germander).

Division D.

Series I.

Calamintha,

rpices of stamens connivent under upper lip of corolla ; tube straight, thirteen-nerved, and hairy inside at the top — (the basil thyme).

LABIATÆ.

Melissa,

stamens connivent ; upper lip of corolla concave ; tube curved—(the balm).

Melttis,

stamens parallel ; upper lip of corolla flat — (the bastard balm).

Prunella,

stamens parallel ; upper lip of corolla flat, angular, and trifid ; filaments toothed below the anther—(the self-heal).

Scutellaria,

stamens parallel ; upper lip of corolla concave and uncut, and with a scale on the back —(the skull cap).

Series II.

Ballota,

calyx ten-ribbed, funnel-shaped, with ovate teeth ; lower stamens longest –(the horehound).

LABIATÆ.

Galeopsis,

calyx bell-shaped ; lower stamens longest ; lower lip of corolla with three lobes and two teeth on its upper side —(the hemp nettle).

Lamium,

calyx bell-shaped ; lower stamens longest ; lower lip of corolla without lobes, but with one or two small teeth on each side—(the dead-nettle).

Leonurus,

calyx tubular ; lower stamens longest ; lower lip of corolla without teeth, the upper lip woolly—(the mother wort).

Nepeta,

calyx tubular, with fifteen parallel ribs ; upper stamens longest— (the ground ivy).

LABIATÆ

Stachys,

calyx bell-shaped, with narrow teeth; lower stamens longest; upper lip of corolla concave, lower lip of three unequal lobes, of which the lateral ones are reflexed—(the betony).

Series III.

Marrubium,

calyx, with ten recurved teeth; lower stamens longest—(the white horehound).

LEGUMINOSÆ.

Plate vii.

Division A—

having nine stamens in a group, and one solitary.

Division B—

having the ten stamens in one group.

Division A—

Series i., leaves of three leaflets.

Series ii., pinnate leaves without terminal leaflet.

Series iii., pinnate leaves with terminal leaflet.

Division B—

Series i., leaves of three leaflets or simple.

Series ii., pinnate leaves.

LEGUMINOSÆ

Division A.

Series I.

Lotus,

flowers in an umbel; calyx teeth equal: keel ascending with a narrowed point; pod straight and many-seeded —(the bird's foot trefoil).

Medicago,

flowers in a short raceme; calyx teeth nearly equal; keel obtuse; pod spiral or falcate, and many-seeded— (the medick).

Melilotus,

flowers in a long raceme; calyx teeth nearly equal; keel obtuse; pod long and nearly straight, and having four seeds or less.

Trifolium,

flowers in heads; calyx teeth unequal; keel obtuse; pod short and straight, and having four seeds or less— (the clover).

Trigonella,

flowers in a short raceme; pod long and curved, and having five or more seeds —(the fenugreek).

LEGUMINOSÆ

Series II.

Lathyrus,

style dilated upwards, flat on the upper side, and hairy beneath the stigma—(the vetchling).

Vicia,

style filiform, and hairy all over—(the vetch).

Series III.

Arthrolobium.

flowers in an umbel and without a pinnate leaf at the apex; pod compressed and many-jointed — (the joint vetch).

Astragalus,

keel obtuse; pod two-celled with the lower suture inflexed—(the milk vetch).

Hippocrepis.

flowers in an umbel; pod of many crescent-shaped joints —(the horse-shoe vetch).

LEGUMINOSÆ.

Onobrychis,

flowers in a raceme; pod flat, with only one joint—(the sainfoin).

Ornithopus,

flowers in an umbel; pod curved and many-jointed—(the bird's foot).

Oxytropus,

keel pointed; pod two-celled, with the upper surface inflexed.

Division B.
Series I.

Genista

calyx with two lips, the upper bifid, the lower trifid; lower leaves simple—(the green weed).

LEGUMINOSÆ.

Ononis,

calyx with five clefts---(the rest harrow).

Sarothamnus,

calyx with two lips, the upper bifid, the lower trifid; lower leaves ternate—(the broom).

Ulex,

calyx with two lips, with two minute bracts at the base —(the furze).

Series II.
Anthyllis,

calyx with five clefts; keel without a beak—(the ladies' finger)

LEMNACEÆ.
Plate xxvii.

Lemna

a water plant; frond with fine hair-like roots—(the duckweed).

I 2

LEMNACEÆ.

Wolffia,

a water plant; frond with no roots.

LENTIBULARI-ACEÆ. Plate xxi.

Pinguicula,

calyx with upper lip three; cleft, lower lip two cleft-leaves entire—(the butter-wort).

Utricularia,

calyx of two equal sepals; leaves multifid; a water plant—(the bladderwort).

LILIACEÆ.
Plate xxv.
Division A—
with fleshy fruits.

Division B—
with dry fruits.

Division A—
Series i., with a simple stem.
Series ii., with a branched stem.

Division B—
Series i., with a leafless scape.
Series ii., with a leafy stem.

LILIACEÆ.
Division A.
Series I.
Convallaria,

perianth bell-shaped ; stem leafless—(the lily of the valley).

Maianthemum,

perianth spreading, divided to the base ; stem with two leaves—(the may lily).

Polygonatum,

flowers axillary ; stem with more than two leaves—(the Solomon's seal).

Series II.
Asparagus,

flowers axillary ; stem erect and herbaceous ; leaves setaceous—(the asparagus).

LILIACEÆ.
Ruscus,

flowers very small and apparently borne on centre of leaves ; stem shrubby ; leaves with spines — (the butcher's broom).

Division B.
Series I.
Allium,

flowers in terminal umbel enclosed in a spathe of one or two leaves—(the garlic).

Gagea,

yellow flowers, sometimes in a corymb, sometimes in an umbel.

Hyacinthus,

segments of perianth cohering at base and reflexed at the tips—(the blue bell).

LILIACEÆ.
Muscari,

perianth with six teeth ; segments cohering at base and contracting at the tips — (the grape hyacinth).

Ornithogalum,

leaves of the perianth distinct ; flowers in a raceme and always white or yellow—(the star of Bethlehem).

Scilla,

leaves of perianth distinct ; flowers in a raceme, and never white or yellow — (the squill).

Simethis,

leaves of perianth distinct ; flowers white inside and purple outside.
Series II.
Fritillaria,

flowers chequered, solitary and drooping—(the fritillary).

LILIACEÆ.
Lilium,

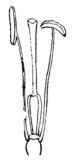

flowers purple, in a panicle, and drooping—(the martagon lily).

Lloydia,

flowers white, with pink lines inside; leaves semi-cylindrical.

Tulipa,

flowers yellow—(the tulip).

LINACEÆ. *Plate* vi.
Linum.

petals, five; sepals, five; stamens, five—(the flax).

LINACEÆ.
Radiola,

petals, four; sepals, four; stamens, four—(the flax seed).

LORANTHACEÆ.
Plate xiii.
Viscum,

petals, four, fleshy and united at the base; leaves opposite; a parasitic plant — (the mistletoe).

LYCOPODIACEÆ.
Plate xxxii.
Isoetes,

no stem; filiform leaves—(the quill wort).

Lycopodium,

long stem; capsules all two-valved—(the club moss).

LYCOPODIACEÆ.
Selaginella,

long stem; capsules two-valved and three-valved.

LYTHRACEÆ.
Plate ix.
Lythrum,

calyx tubular; style filiform—(the purple loosestrife).

Peplis

calyx bell-shaped; style very short—(the water purslane).

MALVACEÆ.
Plate vi.
Althæa.

involucre of five or more lobes—(the marsh mallow).

MALVACEÆ.

Lavatera,

involucre of three lobes—(the tree mallow).

Malva.

involucre of three distinct leaves (the mallow).

MARSILEACEÆ.

Plate xxxii.

Pilularia,

spore clusters globose, hard and solitary, flowerless plant —(the pill-wort).

MELANTHACEÆ.

Plate xxvi.

Colchicum.

scape leafless—(the meadow saffron).

MELANTHACEÆ.

Tofieldia.

scape leafy—(the Scottish asphodel).

MYRICACEÆ.

Plate xxiii.

Myrica

catkins sessile and erect; fruit drupaceous; leaves fragrant—(the sweet gale).

NAIADACEÆ.

Plate xxvii.

Naias,

imperfect flowers, axillary and solitary; stigmas, two or four.

Potamogeton,

flowers perfect; four segments to perianth—(the pondweed).

Ruppia,

flowers perfect, no perianth — (the tassel pond-weed).

NAIADACEÆ.

Zannichellia,

imperfect flowers; one stigma —(the horned pond-weed).

Zostera,

imperfect flowers; flowers in a long sheathing portion of the leaf—(the grass-wrack).

NYMPHÆACEÆ.

Plate i.

Nuphar,

sepals five or six; flowers yellow — (the yellow water lily).

Nymphæa,

sepals four; flowers white— (the white water lily).

OLEACEÆ.

Plate xvii.

Fraxinus,

fruit a pendulous key; leaves pinnate—(the ash tree).

OLEACEÆ.

Ligustrum,

fruit a fleshy berry; simple leaves—(the privet shrub).

ONAGRACEÆ.

Plate ix.

Circæa,

two stamens—(the enchanter's nightshade).

Œnothera,

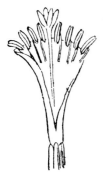

eight stamens, seeds not bearded—(the evening primrose).

Epilobium,

eight stamens; seeds bearded; (the willow herb).

ONAGRACEÆ.

Isnardia,

four stamens.

ORCHIDACEÆ.

Plate xxiv.

Division A—
  without any leaves, except short scales.
Division B—
  with leaves.
Division B—
  Series i., lip spurred.
  Series ii., lip without spur, and hanging.
  Series iii., lip unspurred, and erect or spreading.

Division A.

Corallorhiza,

no spur; lip entire, and not so long as the sepals—(the coral root).

Epipogum,

inflated spur underneath lip; flowers few, large, and pale yellow; stem without leaves.

Neotinea,

small spur; a plate in front of the glands of the pollen masses; flowers pink or purplish.

ORCHIDACEÆ

Neottia,

no spur; lip bi-lobed and longer than the sepals; long column; flowers greyish brown—(the bird's-nest).

Division B.

Series I.

Cypripedium,

anthers, two; flowers very large; lip slipper-shaped and over an inch long — (the lady's slipper).

Gymnadenia,

pollen glands without a pouch; flowers rose-coloured.

Habenaria,

stigma not prolonged between anther cells; flowers white —(the butterfly orchis).

ORCHIDACEÆ.

Orchis,

stigma prolonged between anther cells; pollen glands with a pouch.

Series II.

Aceras,

flowers without stalk; lobes of the lip linear—(the man orchis).

Listera,

flowers with stalk; stem with two opposite broad leaves —(the twayblade).

Ophrys,

flower without stalk; lobes of lip oblong; sepals spreading—(the insect orchis).

Series III.

Cephalanthera,

flowers without stalk, and erect; twisted ovary.

ORCHIDACEÆ.

Epipactis,

flowers with stalk and drooping.

Goodyera,

flowers without stalk and drooping, and all round the spike.

Herminium,

flowers without stalk and drooping, and on one side of a straight spike.

Liparis,

flowers with stalk and erect; lip inferior.

Malaxis,

flowers with stalk and erect; lip superior.

ORCHIDACEÆ.

Spiranthes,

flowers without stalk and drooping, and on one side of a spiral spike.

OROBANCHACEÆ.
Plate xix.

Lathræa,

calyx with four broad short teeth or lobes—(the toothwort).

Orobanche,

calyx deeply divided into two or four pointed sepals—(the broom rape).

OXALIDACEÆ.
Plate vi.

Oxalis,

stamens, ten; styles, five; short and scarcely united at the base—(the wood sorrel).

PAPAVERACEÆ.
Plate ii.

Chelidonium,

fruit linear, single-celled; seeds crested—(the celandim).

PAPAVERACEÆ.
Glaucium.

fruit linear, double-celled; seeds not crested; glaucous foliage—(the horned poppy).

Meconopsis,

fruit oblong; stigma, five or six-rayed, and on a short but distinct style—(the Welsh poppy).

Papaver,

fruit ovate, stigma radiating and on a sessile flat disk—(the poppy).

PLANTAGINACEÆ.
Plate xxi.
Littorella,

flowers unisexual, solitary or two together, the males stalked, the females sessile (the shore-weed).

Plantago,

flowers hermaphrodite and in terminal heads or spikes —(the plantain).

PLUMBAGINACEÆ.
Plate xxi.
Armeria,

flowers in globular heads— (the thrift)

Statice,

flowers in terminal panicles or spikes—(the sea lavender).

POLEMONIACEÆ.
Plate xviii.
Polemonium,

corolla wheel-shaped; tube very short; calyx five-lobed; leaves pinnate—(the Jacob's ladder).

POLYGALACEÆ.
Plate IV.
Polygala,

sepals five, two inner large and wing shaped; stamens eight, in groups of four— (the milk-wort).

POLYGONACEÆ.
Plate xxii.
Oxyria,

perianth of four segments— (the mountain sorrel).

Polygonum,

perianth of five segments; root with a double twist— (the bistort).

Rumex,

perianth of six segments— (the dock).

PORTULACEÆ.
Plate x.
Montia,

corolla five-parted, with three segments smaller than the others, and split down one side—(the blinks).

PRIMULACEÆ.
Plate xxi.
Division A— leaves all radical.

Division B— leaves alternate.

Division C— leaves opposite.

Division D— leaves pectinate.

PRIMULACEÆ.
Division A.
Cyclamen,

tube of corolla nearly globular; limb reflexed — (the sow-bread).

Primula,

tube of corolla cylindrical; lobes spreading—(the primrose).

Division B.
Samolus,

all leaves alternate; capsule half inferior, opening with five valves — (the brookweed).

Trientalis,

a terminal whorl of leaves; calyx with seven lobes—(the trientale).

Division C.
Anagallis,

stamens, five; capsule opening transversely; flowers, pink or scarlet—(the pimpernel).

PRIMULACEÆ.
Centunculus,

stamens, four — (the chaffweed).

Glaux,

stamens, five; no corolla— (the sea milkwort).

Lysimachia,

stamens, five; capsule opening at the top; flowers yellow —(the loosestrife).

Division D.
Hottonia,

a water plant; leaves all submerged—(the water violet).

RANUNCULACEÆ.
Plate i.

Division A—
regular flowers.

Division B—
regular flowers, but no corolla.

Division C—
irregular flowers.

RANUNCULACEÆ.
Division A.
Actæa,

petals, four; sepals, four; introrse anthers; stamens rising from a glandular disk; leaves like elder leaves — (the herb-Christopher).

Adonis,

petals, five to ten; sepals, five, and petaloid; flowers scarlet —(the pheasant's eye).

Aquilegia,

spurred petals—(the columbine).

Eranthis,

petals, five, tubular; sepals, five, deciduous; leafy involucre — (the **winter aconite**).

Helleborus,

petals, eight or ten, tubular; sepals, five, persistent— (the hellebore).

RANUNCULACEÆ.

Myosurus,

petals, five; sepals, five; stamens five; flowers spicate and very small—(the mousetail).

Ranunculus,

petals, five, with a little scale or thickened hollow spot at the base; sepals, five; carpels, single seeded — (the buttercup).

NoE.—Ranunculus ficaria has a small rootstock bearing annually a number of tubers—(the pilewort).

Trolliur,

sepals, five or many; petals, from five to fifteen, small, flat and linear—(the globe flower).

Division B.
Anemone,

involucre of three large deeply-cut leaves some distance down the flower stalk,

RANUNCULACEÆ.

Caltha,

sepals, five, bright yellow—(the marsh marigold).

Clematis,

sepals, four to six; a climbing plant, with leaf-stalks serving as tendrils—(the traveller's joy).

Thalictrum,

sepals, four or five, and imbricated in æstivation; stamens longer than the sepals —(the meadow rue).

Division C.
Aconitum,

upper sepals hooded; carpels grouped—(the monkshood).

Delphinium,

upper sepals spurred; carpels solitary—(the larkspur).

RESEDACEÆ
Plate iv.

Reseda,

sepals, four to six; petals, four to six, small, narrow, and generally divided—(the mignonette).

RESTIACEÆ.
Plate xxvii.

Eriocaulon,

perianth of four or six segments, inner ones united; flowers minute and in globular head — (the pipe wort).

RHAMNACEÆ.
Plate vi.

Rhamnus,

calyx with four or five teeth; petals, none, or very small; fruit, a small berry—(the buckthorn).

ROSACEÆ.
Plate viii.

Division A—
having no petals.

Division B—
fruit, a solitary drupe.

Division C—
fruit, a group of follicles.

Division D—
fruit of small dry or succulent nuts.

Division E—
fruit, a pome

ROSACEÆ.

Division D—

Series i., nuts inserted on a dry, fleshy, or succulent receptacle.

Series ii., nuts enclosed in the fleshy tube of the calyx.

Division A.

Alchemilla,

stamens, one to four; calyx eight-parted; style from near the base of the nut—(the lady's mantle).

Poterium,

stamens, many; calyx, four-cleft; nuts, two or three in the dry tube of the calyx—(the burnet).

Sanguisorba,

stamens, four; calyx, four-cleft; nuts, two in the dry tube of the calyx—(the great burnet).

Division B.

Prunus,

petals, five; calyx, five-cleft and deciduous; styles, one to five; nut of the drupe smooth or slightly seamed—(the plum)

ROSACEÆ.

Division C.

Spiræa,

calyx, five-cleft; stamens many; fruit on the calyx tube—(the meadow-sweet).

Division D.

Series I.

Agrimonia,

calyx, five, armed with hooked bristles; petals, five; stamens, fifteen; nuts, two, in the dry tube of the calyx—(the agrimony).

Comarum

flowers purple; calyx, ten-cleft in two rows; petals, five; receptacle large, fleshy, and spongy—(the marsh cinquefoil).

Dryas,

calyx, eight to ten-cleft in one row; petals, eight or ten; nuts tipped with hairy styles, straight at the end—(the mountain aven).

ROSACEÆ.

Fragaria,

calyx, ten-cleft in two rows; petals, five; receptacle large, succulent, and having the nuts sunk in it—(the strawberry).

Geum,

calyx, ten-cleft in two rows; petals, five; nuts tipped with jointed styles hooked at the end—(the avens).

Potentilla,

calyx ten-cleft in two rows; petals, four or five; stamens many; seeds without bristles on a flattish dry receptacle —(the cinquefoil).

Rubus,

calyx five-cleft; petals, five; stamens, many; styles, many; fruit, succulent drupaceous, on a conical spongy receptacle — (the blackberry).

ROSACEÆ.

Sibbaldia,

calyx ten-cleft in two rows; petals, five, and small; stamens, five; fruit on a dry receptacle.

Series II.

Rosa,

calyx urn-shaped, contracted at the mouth and ultimately fleshy; petals, four or five; stamens many; styles many —(the dog rose).

Division E.

Cotoneaster,

calyx, five; petals, five; styles, two to five; fruit not cohering at the centre.

Cratægus,

calyx segments acute; fruit oval, hiding upper end of the bony carpels — (the hawthorn).

ROSACEÆ.

Mespilus,

calyx segments leafy; fruit turbinate, and exposing upper end of the bony carpels—(the medlar).

Pyrus,

calyx, five; petals, five; styles, two to five; fruit with five cartilaginous double-seeded cells—(the apple).

RUBIACEÆ.

Plate xiii.

Asperula,

corolla funnel-shaped; fruit dry, double lobed, double seeded, and not crowned with the limb of the calyx —(the woodruff).

Galium,

no calyx; corolla wheel-shaped, with four teeth; fruit dry, not crowned with the calyx—(the bedstraw).

RUBIACEÆ.

Rubia,

no calyx; corolla wheel-shaped, with five teeth; fruit fleshy; flowers yellow —(the madder).

Sherardia,

no calyx; corolla bell-shaped, with six teeth; fruit crowned with the calyx; flowers lilac — (the field madder).

SALICACEÆ.

Plate xxiii.

Populus,

catkins with jagged scales; stamens, eight or more— (the poplar).

Salix,

catkins with entire imbricated scales; stamens, five or less — (the willow).

SANTALACEÆ.

Plate xxii.

Thesium,

perianth funnel-shaped and five-cleft; stamens, five— (the bastard toad flax).

SAXIFRAGACEÆ.

Plate x.

Chrysosplenium.

no petals; calyx four-cleft; stamens, eight; capsule single-celled, with two beaks—(the golden saxifrage)

Parnassia,

five petals, each with a short claw; stamens, five, with five fringed scales interposed; stigmas four—(the grass of Parnassus).

Saxifraga,

petals, five; stamens, ten; capsule double-celled, opening between the beaks.

SCLERANTHACEÆ.

Plate x.

Scleranthus,

perianth five-cleft, contracted at mouth; stamens, ten or five, inserted in the mouth of the calyx—(the knawel).

SCROPHULARI-ACEÆ.

Plate xviii.

Division A—
having two stamens, and corolla, four or five-cleft.

Division B—
having four stamens, two long and two short and calyx four-cleft.

Division C—
having four or five stamens, and calyx five-cleft.

Division A.

Veronica,

corolla wheel-shaped, lower lobe the longest; capsules compressed and double-celled—(the speedwell).

Division B.

Bartsia,

corolla tubular and ringent, upper lip not flattened, and entire.

SCROPHULARI-ACEÆ.

Euphrasia,

corolla tubular and two-lipped, upper lip flattened and bifid—(the eyebright).

Melampyrum,

calyx tubular and toothed; corolla ringent, upper lip flattened, with reflexed margins—(the cow-wheat).

Rhinanthus,

calyx inflated, teeth small; corolla ringent, and upper lip flattened; seeds with an orbicular margin—(the yellow rattle).

Division C.

Antirrhinum,

corolla personate; gibbous at the base; no distinct spur— (the snapdragon).

SCROPHULARI-ACEÆ.

Digitalis,

corolla bell - shaped and oblique ; leaves alternate— (the foxglove).

Limosella,

corolla bell-shaped and equal and five - cleft ; flowers white—(the mud wort).

Linaria,

corolla personate and spurred, with a prominent palate closing the mouth — (the toad flax).

Mimulus,

corolla ringent ; upper lip with reflexed sides ; leaves opposite.

SCROPHULARI-ACEÆ.

Pedicularis,

calyx inflated and five-toothed; corolla ringent ; upper lip compressed laterally; lower plane three-lobed ; capsules obtuse—(the red rattle).

Scrophularia,

corolla globose, with five un-equal lobes—(the fig wort).

Sibthorpia,

corolla wheel - shaped and irregularly five-cleft ; leaves orbicular and alternate— (the money wort).

Verbascum,

corolla wheel - shaped ; sta-mens, five—(the mullein).

SOLANACEÆ.
Plate xviii.

Atropa,

corolla bell-shaped ; anthers do not open by pores ; fruit globose—(the deadly night-shade).

SOLANACEÆ.

Hyoscyamus,

corolla funnel-shaped, with five unequal lobes ; anthers burst longitudinally ; cap-sule opening transversely by a convex lid—(the hen-bane).

Solanum,

corolla wheel-shaped ; anthers connivent, opening by two apical pores — (the night-shade).

TAMARISCACEÆ.
Plate ix.

Tamarix,

calyx, four or five parted ; petals, four or five; stamens four or five, or eight or ten, on a hypogynous ring ; styles three ; stigmas fea-thery—(the tamarisk).

THYMELACEÆ.
Plate xxii.

Daphne,

perianth four-cleft ; stamens, eight, inserted in two rows ; berry fleshy — (the meze-reon).

TILIACEÆ.
Plate vi.
Tilia,

sepals, five ; petals, five ; stamens, many ; ovary, five-celled—(the lime tree).

TRILLIACEÆ.
Plate xxvi.
Paris,

perianth in two whorls ; outer herbaceous, inner coloured ; leaves, four, in a whorl—(the herb Paris).

TYPHACEÆ.
Plate xxvii.
Sparganium,

flowers in globular heads —(the bur weed).

Typha,

flowers in dense cylindrical spikes—(the bulrush).

ULMACEÆ.
Plate xxiii.
Ulmus,

flower perfect ; perianth bell-shaped and persistent, four or five-cleft ; stamens, five ; styles, two—(the elm).

UMBELLIFERÆ.
Plates xi, xii, xiii.

Division A—
simple or irregular umbels.
Division B—
compound umbels.
Division B—
Series i., fruit prickly.
Series ii., fruit beaked.
Series iii., fruit not prickly or beaked, but flattened and united by their faces.
Series iv., fruit not prickly or beaked, but flattened and united by the narrow edge.
Series v., fruit neither flattened nor prickly nor beaked.

Division A.
Astrantia,

calyx of five leafy teeth ; fruit with five plicate-dentate ridges ; involucral bracts large and coloured ; palmate leaves.

Eryngium,

spiny palmate leaves — (the eryngo).

UMBELLIFERÆ.
Hydrocotyle,

peltate leaves ; creeping stem (the pennywort).

Sanicula,

flowers in panicled tufts ; the outer without stamens ; the inner without pistils ; leaves palmate ; fruit round and prickly—(the sanicle).

Division B.
Series 1.
Caucalis,

fruit with hooked bristles ; compound leaves — (the bur parsley).

Daucas,

fruit with prominent ridges ; compressed leaves ; bracts pinnatifid—(the carrot).

UMBELLIFERÆ.
Torilis,

fruit with straight bristles; compound leaves — (the hedge parsley).

Series II.
Anthriscus,

beak slender, shorter than the fruit—(the beaked parsley).

Chærophyllum,

beak very short; carpels obtusely ribbed; vittæ single —(the chervil).

Myrrhis,

beak very short; carpels acutely ribbed; no vittæ— (the cicely).

Scandix,

beak long; carpels with five blunt ridges — (the shepherd's needle).

UMBELLIFERÆ.
Series III.
Angelica,

fruit with three sharp ridges at the back of each carpel, and two at the sides; fruit dorsally compressed; lateral wings separate.

Heracleum,

petals obcordate with an inflexed point, outer ones radiant; fruit with even wings; lower leaves pinnate, upper leaves lobed—(the cow-parsnip).

Pastinaca,

petals entire and acute; fruit with even wings; flowers small and yellow — (the parsnip).

Peucedanum,

petals obcordate; fruit with a thin flat margin, lateral ridges at the base of the wings; lower leaves of three large three-lobed segments with equal stalks— (the hog's fennel).

UMBELLIFERÆ.
Tordylium,

fruit with a thick wrinkled margin; lower leaves pinnate; upper leaves pinnatifid—(the hart wort).

Series IV.
Ægopodium,

fruit oblong, with five filiform ridges; interstices without vittæ; no involucres—(the gout weed).

Apium,

fruit ovate, with five prominent ridges; vittæ solitary; umbels mostly lateral and sessile—(the celery)

Bunium,

petals emarginate; fruit oblong, crowned with the conical base of the erect styles; vittæ, many: leaves compound—(the earth nut).

K

UMBELLIFERÆ.

Bupleurum,

leaves simple, linear or ovate —(the hare's ear).

Carum,

petals emarginate; fruit oblong; base of style depressed; vittæ solitary; leaves compound — (the caraway).

Conium,

petals emarginate; fruit ovate, glabrous, with five prominent wavy ridges; no vittæ; leaves compound—(the hemlock).

Cicuta,

calyx of five leafy teeth; petals obcordate, with an inflexed point; fruit with obscure ridges; vittæ solitary—(the cow bane).

Helosciadium,

fruit egg-shaped; interstices with single vittæ — (the marsh wort).

UMBELLIFERÆ.

Petroselinum,

petals entire; bracts, many; flowers yellow; fruit egg-shaped; single vittæ; compound leaves—(the parsley).

Physospermum,

fruit of two bladder-like lobes, with five filiform slender equal ridges, the lateral within the margin; solitary vittæ; compound leaves—(the bladder seed).

Pimpinella,

no involucral bracts; fruit oblong, crowned with the swollen base of the reflexed styles; pinnate leaves, upper ones occasionally pinnatifid — (the burnet saxifrage).

Sison,

petals emarginate; fruit egg-shaped with blunt ridges; clavate vittæ; leaves pinnate, upper ones very narrow—(the stone parsley).

UMBELLIFERÆ.

Sium,

leaves all pinnate—(the water parsnip).

Smyrnium,

fruit orbicular, with three prominent ridges; vittæ many—(the alexanders).

Trinia,

flowers diœcious; petals yellow; leaflets linear; fruit with five ridges with a single vitta beneath each of them —(the honewort)

Series V.
Æthusa,

petals obcordate with an acute inflexed point; fruit globose, with five-keeled ridges crowned with the reflexed styles; single vittæ —(the fool's parsley).

Coriandrum.

outer petals radiant and bifid; fruit globular, with obscure ridges; no vittæ — (the coriander).

UMBELLIFERÆ.
Crithmum,

petals elliptical, entire, and involute; fruit with triangular sharp ridges, and said to resemble barley; leaves compound and fleshy —(the samphire).

Fœniculum,

petals entire, roundish, with a broad obtuse inflexed lobe; fruit oblong, with five bluntly-keeled ridges; style short; single vittæ; very finely - cut leaves — (the fennel)

Ligusticum,

petals ovate, acutely emarginate, with an inflexed lobe and a short claw; fruit elliptical, with five winged ridges; numerous vittæ— (the lovage).

Meum,

petals entire, elliptical, acute at both ends, with an incurved point—(the spignel).

Œnanthe,

fruit sessile, egg-shaped, with long erect styles; umbels of ten to twenty rays—(the water dropwort).

UMBELLIFERÆ.
Seseli,

umbels of more than twenty rays; fruit hairy, with thick ribs and long reflexed styles —(the meadow saxifrage).

Silaus,

petals yellow, appendaged at the base — (the pepper saxifrage).

URTICACEÆ.
Plate xxiii.
Humulus,

stamens five; flowers diœcious; males in loose panicles in the upper axils; females in catkins with ovate scales; stigmas two, long and linear; opposite leaves; a tall climbing plant — (the hop).

Parietaria,

stamens four; flowers polygamous, surrounded by an involucre, and in axillary clusters; leaves alternate; hairs simple — (the wall pellitory).

URTICACEÆ.
Urtica,

stamens four; flowers monœcious or diœcious; males in loose racemes, with perianth four-parted; females in capitate racemes, with perianth two-parted; stigma sessile; opposite leaves; stinging hairs—(the stinging nettle).

VACCINIACEÆ.
Plate xvii.
Vaccinium,

disk epigynous; leaves alternate—(the whortleberry).

VALERIANACEÆ.
Plate xiii.
Centranthus,

one stamen; corolla fivelobed, and having a spur— (the spur valerian).

Valeriana,

three stamens; corolla gibbous, swollen but not spurred; fruit single-celled, with feathery pappus—(the valerian).

VALERIANACEÆ.

Valerianella,

three stamens; fruit three-celled, crowned with the erect irregularly - toothed limb of the calyx — (the corn salad).

VERBENACEÆ.
Plate xix.

Verbena,

calyx five-cleft; corolla tubular, irregular, five-lobed, and slightly two-lipped; stamens four or two included in the tube—(the vervain).

VIOLACEÆ.
Plate iv.

Viola,

sepals five, extended at the base; petals five, unequal, the lower one extended into a hollow spur behind; stamens five, filaments very short and broad — (the violet).

510

524

INDEX III.

THE SPECIES.

◆

I N this list only such particulars are given as are needed to distinguish one species from another. For the characteristics of the genera reference must be made to the preceding index. The species chosen for illustration in the coloured plates are shown by the asterisks.

Bupleurum, Plate xii. 173.
aristatum—yellow, sharp-pointed bracts.
falcatum—yellow, elliptical long-stalked leaves.
*rotundifolium—yellow, yellowish oval bracts, perfoliate leaves.
tenuissimum—yellow, awl-shaped bracts.

Butomus, Plate xxvii. 436.
*umbellatus — rose, leaves radical, linear, ensiform and twisted at point.

Buxus, Plate xxiii. 366.
*sempervirens—cream, shining oblong leaves.

Cakile, Plate ii. 25.
*maritima—purple, zigzag branches.

Calamagrostis, Plate xxx. 481.
epigejos—erect, close panicle, hairs longer than paleæ.
*lanceolata—loose panicle.
stricta—erect close panicle, hairs shorter than paleæ.

Calamintha, Plate xix. 308.
acinos—purple, whorls five or six flowered.
clinopodium — purple, straggling stem, leaves egg-shaped and stalked.
nepeta—purple, prominent hairs on calyx mouth.
*officinalis—purple, erect stem, hairs on calyx mouth included.

Callitriche, Plate ix. 132.
autumnalis—no bracts, fruit-lobes winged.
*verna—falcate bracts, fruit-lobes keeled.

Calluna, Plate xvii. 262.
*vulgaris—pale rose, leaves in four rows.

Caltha, Plate i. 8.
*palustris—yellow, imbricate sepals.
radicans—yellow, stem rooting at joints.
vulgaris—yellow, stem not rooting.

Camelina, Plate iii. 38.
*sativa—yellow, stem leaves arrow-shaped.

Campanula, Plate xvi. 256.
glomerata—dark blue, angled stem, flowers in clusters.
hederacea—pale blue, thread-like stem, leaves toothed.
hybrida—purple, rough wiry stem, waved leaves, sessile flowers.
latifolia—deep blue, tall furrowed leafy stem, hairy flowers.
patula—blue, rough angled stem, flowers in loose panicles.
persicifolia—blue, large flowers, round stem, smooth leaves.
rapunculus—pale blue, tall, angled stem, small flowers.
rapunculoides—pale purple, creeping stem, flowers on one side.
*rotundifolia—light blue, smooth slender stem, radical leaves reniform.
trachelium—blue, rough angled stem, lower leaves cordate.

Capsella, Plate ii. 30.
*bursa pastoris — white, triangular heart-shaped pods.

Cardamine, Plate iii. 42.
amara—white, anthers lilac.
hirsuta—white, four stamens.
impatiens—white, fringed stipules.
*pratensis—pale lilac, anthers yellow.

Carduus, Plate xv. 228.
acaulis—purple, no stem, or very short one, smooth leaves.
arvensis—purple, stem not winged, creeping rootstock.
crispus—purple, heads clustered and round.
eriophorus—lilac, stem not winged, heads large and cottony.
heterophyllus—pink, heads large and solitary, stem branched and cottony.
lanceolatus — purple, winged stem, ovate cottony involucre.
marianus — purple, large flowers, leaves white veined.
*nutans—purple, heads solitary and drooping, bracts cottony.
palustris—purple, winged stem.
pratensis—purple, leaves waved at edge, cobwebbed terminal heads.
tenuiflorus — lilac, heads clustered and cylindrical.
tuberosus — purple, leaves sessile, stem without wing or prickles.

Carex, Plate xxviii. 464.
acuta—two or three barren spikelets, leaf margin revolute, fruit ribbed.
ampullacea—three stigmas, fertile spikelets stout and drooping, fruit inflated, leaves grooved.
aquatilis—terminal spikelets barren, leaf margin involute, fruit not veined.
arenaria—simple alternate spikelets on interrupted spike.
atrata—stalked terminal spikelets with barren and fertile flowers.
axillaris—nearly sessile spikelets, barren at base, long bracteas, flat leaves.
binervis—two green ribs on outer surface of smooth ovate fruit.
capillaris—three stigmas, fertile spikelets drooping, bracts without sheaths.
clandestina—three stigmas, fertile spikelets erect, bracts sheathing, fruit hairy, leaves involute.
curta—six whitish elliptical spikelets barren at base.
depauperata—beak of large globular fruit long and bifid.
digitata—three stigmas, fertile spikelets erect, bract sheathing, fruit hairy, leaves revolute.
dioica—diœcious, two stigmas.
distans—solitary barren spikelets, erect fertile spikelets, upper stalks in bract sheath.
divisa—simple alternate spikelets in crowded head with leafy bract.
divulsa — simple alternate distant spikes barren at top, tufted root.
elongata—many oblong spikelets barren at base, no bracts.
extensa—solitary barren spikelets, erect fertile spikelets, convolute leaves.
filiformis—solitary barren spikelet, stalked fertile spikelets, grooved slender leaves.
flava—solitary barren spikelets, erect fertile spikelets, long, leafy, sheathing bracts.
fulva—solitary barren spikelets, erect fertile spikelets, upper stalks beyond bract sheath.
hirta—solitary barren spikelets, sessile fertile spikelets, flat hairy leaves.
incurva—capitate compound spikelet, barren at top.

Carex, Plate xxviii. (*cont.*).
lævigata—beak of streaked ovate fruit, long, bifid, and rough edged.
limosa — three stigmas, fertile spikelets drooping, bracts auricled.
montana—three stigmas, fertile spikelets sessile, bracts small, fruit hairy.
muricata—oval spike of compact alternate simple spikelets, barren at top.
ovalis—six alternate ovate spikelets, barren at base.
pallescens — three stigmas, fertile spikes erect, glabrous fruit.
paludosa—five stigmas, three fertile spikelets stout and erect, fruit not inflated.
*paniculata—spikelet thrice compound, barren at top.
paradoxa—long panicled spikelet, barren at top, stem with convex sides.
pauciflora—three stigmas, solitary spikelet top flowers barren.
pendula—three stigmas, fertile spikelets long stalked and drooping, bracts sheathing.
pilulifera—three stigmas, fertile spikelets round and sessile, bracts awl-shaped.
præcox—three stigmas, fertile spikelets sessile, bracts clasping, fruit hairy.
pseudocyperus—three stigmas, fertile spikelets, stout and drooping, fruit not inflated.
pulicaris—two stigmas, solitary spikelet, top barren.
punctata—pellucid spots on ovate, tumid fruit.
rariflora—three stigmas, fertile spikelets drooping, bracts with sheaths.
remota—nearly sessile spikelets, barren at base, long bracts, grooved leaves.
rigida—one barren spikelet, leaf margin revolute, fruit not ribbed.
riparia—three stigmas, pointed and erect, fertile spikelets, fruit not inflated, convex on both sides.
rupestris—three stigmas, solitary spikelet, top barren.
saxatilis—two stigmas, fertile spikelets stout and drooping.
stellulata—three or four roundish spikelets, barren at base.
stricta—one barren spikelet, leaf margin revolute, fruit veined.
strigosa—barren spikelets solitary, fertile, drooping and slender, fruit smooth.
sylvatica—barren spikelets solitary, fertile drooping and filiform, fruit smooth.
teretiuscula—compact panicled spike, barren at top, stem with convex sides.
tomentosa—three stigmas, fertile spikelets stalked, bracts leaf-like, fruit downy.
vahlii—sessile terminal spikelets with barren and fertile flowers.
vesicaria—three stigmas, fertile spikelets, stout and drooping, fruit inflated, leaves flat.
vulgaris—terminal spikelets barren, leaf margin involute, fruit veined.
vulpina—dense panicled spike, barren at top, stem with hollow sides.

Carlina,   Plate xv. 230.
*vulgaris — red, inner bracts petal-like, and straw coloured.

Carpinus,   Plate xxiii. 374.
betulus—oval, doubly toothed leaves.

Carum,   Plate xi. 169.
bulbo castanum—white, tuberous root.
*carui—white, fusiform root.
verticillatum—white, fascicled root.

Catabrosa,   Plate xxx. 491.
*aquatica — pyramidal panicle, whorled branches.

Caucalis,   Plate xiii. 188.
*daucoides—white, furrowed stem, joints hairy.
latifolia—pink, rough stem, pinnate leaves.

Centaurea,   Plate xv. 231.
calcitrapa—rose, spinous involucre, heads lateral.
*cyanus—blue, outer bracts deeply toothed.
nigra—purple, outer bracts fringed with bristles.
scabiosa—purple, pinnatifid leaves, bracts downy.
solstitialis—yellow, spinous involucre, heads terminal.

Centranthus,   Plate xiii. 204.
*ruber—red, spurred corolla.

Centunculus,   Plate xxi. 341.
*minimus—pink, alternate egg-shaped leaves.

Cephalanthera,   Plate xxiv. 389.
ensifolia—white, lanceolate leaves.
*grandiflora—cream, ovate leaves.
rubra—rose, lanceolate leaves.

Cerastium,   Plate v. 74.
alpinum—white, white silky leaves.
aquaticum — white, large heart-shaped leaves.
*arvense—white, petals twice as long as sepals.
glomeratum — white, sepals longer than petals, narrow bluish leaves.
latifolium—white, yellowish downy leaves.
semidecandrum—white, five stamens.
tetrandrum—white, four stamens.
triviale—white, sepals longer than petals, ovate leaves.

Ceratophyllum,   Plate ix. 133.
*demersum—dark green leaves.
submersum—pale green leaves.

Ceterach,   Page 132, 510.
*officinarum — pinnæ covered at back with chaffy scales.

Chærophyllum,   Plate xiii. 192
*temulentum—white, stem with swollen joints and spotted hairs.

Cheiranthus,   Plate iv. 48.
*cheiri—yellow, rib on each valve of pod, shrubby stem.

Chelidonium,   Plate ii. 21.
*majus—yellow, flowers in long umbels.

Chenopodium,   Plate xxii. 349.
album—green, leaves mealy below
*bonus henricus—green, leaves triangular, hastate, entire.
botryoides—green, prostrate stem, triangular leaves.
filicifolium—green, leaves glaucous below.
glaucum—green, prostrate stem, toothed leaves mealy below.
hybridum—green, leaves cordate, green below.
murale — green, leaves ovate, unequal, toothed, green below.

Prunella, Plate xx. 320.
*vulgaris — purplish blue, head with two leaves at base.

Prunus, Plate viii. 108.
avium—white flowers in umbels, drooping.
cerasus—white, flowers in umbels, erect.
domestica—white, flowers solitary, leaf-ribs downy.
insititia—white, flowers solitary, drooping,
padus — white, flowers in raceme, leaves smooth.
*spinosa—white, flowers solitary, erect, very thorny.

Pseudathyrium, Plate xxxiii. 506.
*alpestre—pinnules sharply toothed.

Pteris, Page 88, 520.
*aquilina—marginal sori.

Pulmonaria, Plate xx. 331.
*angustifolia—pink, lanceolate leaves.
officinalis—purple, spotted cordate leaves.

Pyrola, Plate xvii. 268.
*media—white, spiral triangular flower stalk.
minor—rose, square flower stalk, flowers in slender cluster.
rotundifolia — white, straight triangular flower stalk.
secunda—white, flowers drooping in dense cluster all one way.
uniflora — white, large fragrant solitary flower.

Pyrus, Plate viii. 125.
aria—white, leaves white felted beneath.
aucuparia—white, flowers in corymb, pinnate leaves.
communis — white, flowers in corymb, elliptic serrate leaves.
*malus—pink, flowers in umbel, leaves ovate, acute, serrate.
torminalis — white, leaf-lobes triangular, lower ones spreading.

Quercus, Plate xxiii. 372.
*robur—the oak tree, leaves sinuate and lobed.

Radiola, Plate vi. 77.
*millegrana—white, very small plant, forked stem.

Ranunculus, Plate i. 6, 7.
acris—yellow, round smooth stalk.
*aquatilis—white, floating leaves trifid, others capilliform.
arvensis—pale yellow, spreading calyx, large carpels, prickly achenes.
auricomus—yellow, lower leaves reniform upper leaves divided, unfurrowed stalk.
bulbosus—yellow, reflexed calyx, furrowed stem.
*ficaria—yellow, cordate leaves.
flammula—yellow, decumbent stem, ovate leaves.
hederaceus—white reniform leaves broad at base.
hirsutus—yellow, erect hairy stem.
lenormandi—white, reniform leaves narrow at base.
lingua—yellow, large flowers, sessile lanceolate leaves.

RANUNCULUS, Plate i. (*cont.*).
ophioglossifolius—yellow, erect stem, ovate leaves.
parviflorus—yellow, decumbent hairy stem.
repens — yellow, furrowed stalk, creeping stem.
sceleratus—pale yellow, hairy reflexed calyx.

Raphanus, Plate iv. 54.
maritimus—yellow, lyrate bristly leaves.
*raphanistrum—whitish yellow, root leaves interruptedly lyrate.

Reseda, Plate iv. 55.
lutea—yellow, sepals and petals six.
*luteola—yellow, sepals and petals four.
suffruticulosa—white, sepals and petals five.

Rhamnus, Plate vi. 89.
*catharticus—yellowish, branches spinous
frangula—white, flowers five-cleft.

Rhinanthus, Plate xviii. 290.
*cristagalli—yellow, green bracts.
major—yellow, yellow bracts.

Rhyncospora, Plate xxviii. 457.
*alba—white, two stamens.
fusca—brown, three stamens.

Ribes, Plate x. 144.
alpinum— green, glabrous calyx, flowers erect.
grossularia — green, thorny stem, small bracts.
*nigrum—green, downy calyx, flowers drooping and downy.
rubrum—green, smooth calyx, flowers drooping and smooth.

Rosa, Plate viii. 117.
arvensis—white, scentless flowers, trailing stem, fruit subglobose with convex disc.
canina — pink, smooth leaves, hooked prickles, sepals reflexed after fall of corolla.
inodora—rose, doubly serrate downy leaves, hooked prickles, sepals closely pinnate.
involuta— pink, hairy doubly serrate leaves, round fruit, no disc, prickles passing into aciculi.
micrantha—pale rose, doubly serrate downy leaves, uniform hooked prickles, hairy stalk.
mollis—rose, shoots erect, glandulose leaves, straight prickles, ovate leaves, slightly pinnate sepals.
*rubiginosa—rose, hairy leaves, fragrant round at base, prickles mixed, fruit pear-shaped, disc small.
sæpium—rose, hairy leaves, acute at base, prickles mixed, long lax branches, stalk naked, styles hairy.
spinosissima — pink, erect, bent shoots, crowded prickles simple sepals, leaves smooth, fruit black, round and erect.
systyla — pale pink, shoots erect, bent, prickles equal and hooked, fruit, ovate with large disc.
tomentosa — rose, shoots arched, downy elliptic leaves, straight prickles, sepals copiously pinnate.

Rubia, Plate xiii. 200.
*peregrina — yellow, leaves rough and in whorls.

M